It's another Quality Book from CGP

This book is for anyone doing AQA Modular GCSE Maths at Intermediate Level.

It contains lots of tricky questions designed to make you sweat — because that's the only way you'll get any better.

It's also got some daft bits in to try and make the whole experience at least vaguely entertaining for you.

What CGP is all about

Our sole aim here at CGP is to produce the highest quality books — carefully written, immaculately presented and dangerously close to being funny.

Then we work our socks off to get them out to you — at the cheapest possible prices.

Contents

Don't panic! We haven't forgotten about Modules Two and Four — they're coursework modules, so you don't need to revise them for the exams.

Module One

Module Three

Module Five

Published by Coordination Group Publications Ltd.
Illustrated by Lex Ward and Ashley Tyson

Coordinated by June Hall and Mark Haslam

Contributors:
Gill Allen
JE Dodds
Mark Haslam
Claire Thompson
Dave Williams

Updated by:
Tim Major
Mark Moody
Alan Rix

ISBN 1 84146 096 6

Groovy website: www.cgpbooks.co.uk

Printed by Elanders Hindson, Newcastle upon Tyne.
Clipart sources: CorelDRAW and VECTOR.

Questions on Simple Probability

If you're struggling with Simple Probability, have another look at P.1 of the revision guide for some handy hints.

PROBABILITIES are always between 0 and 1

1) You should express probabilities as a fraction or a decimal.
2) A probability of ZERO means that it will definitely not happen.
3) A probability of ONE means it will definitely happen.

Q1 The number line opposite is a probability scale. Place the letters where you think the following statements lie, in terms of the chance of the event happening.

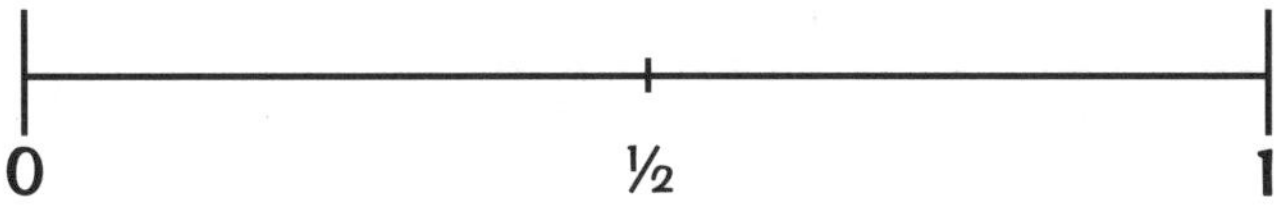

a) The probability of getting a head on a toss of a 10p piece.
b) The probability of choosing a red ball from a bag containing 2 red balls and 1 green ball.
c) The probability of shaking a five on an ordinary dice.
d) The probability of choosing a Guatemalan stamp from a bag containing 60 British stamps and 40 French stamps.

Q2 In a game of Bingo what are the chances of pulling out the 15 ball when a ball is drawn at random from the machine containing the balls 1 to 49 inclusive?

SHORTHAND NOTATION

1) P(x) = 0.25 simply means "the probability of event x happening is 0.25".
2) Eg: if you roll a dice, the probability of rolling a 6 will be written as P(rolls a 6).

Q3 After 49 tosses of an unbiased coin, 24 have been heads and 25 have been tails. What is P(50th toss will be a head)?

Q4 If the probability of picking a banana from a fruit bowl is 0.27, what is the probability of picking something which is not a banana?

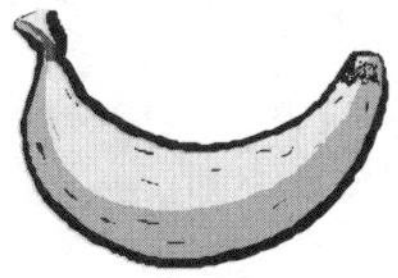

Q5 A bag contains 3 red balls, 4 blue balls and 5 green balls. A ball is chosen at random from the bag. What is the probability that:
a) it is green
b) it is blue
c) it is red
d) it is not red?

Q6 The probability of it raining during the monsoon is ¾, on a particular day.
a) What is the probability of it not raining?
b) If a monsoon 'season' lasts approximately 100 days, how many days are likely to be dry?

Q7 Students at school conduct a survey of the colours of parents' cars, where every parent owns one car. The table shows the results.

Red	Blue	Yellow	White	Green	Other
40	29	13	20	16	14

a) What is the probability of a parent owning a red car?
b) What is the probability of a parent owning a car that is not blue or green?

Questions on Compound Probability

"Compound" or "Combined" Probability is when there are two or more events. Get stuck into this little lot...

Q1 An unbiased six-sided dice is to be thrown and then a three-colour spinner is to be spun. The dice has sides numbered 1, 1, 2, 3, 4, 5 and the spinner has equal sections for red and yellow, but ½ the spinner is blue.

a) Complete the table to show the possible outcomes.

b) What is the most likely outcome?

c) What is the probability of this outcome?

d) What is the probability (R, even)?

e) What is the probability (any colour, 5)?

Die → Spinner ↓	1	1	2	3	4	5
Red	(R,1)					
Yellow	(Y,1)				(Y,4)	
Blue	(B,1)					
Blue	(B,1)					

Q2 A four-edged spinner has numbers 6, 7, 8 and 9. A three-edged spinner has numbers 3, 4 and 5 on it.

a) Complete the table to show all the possible scores when both spinners are spun together and their scores multiplied.

b) What is the probability of achieving the maximum score?

c) What is the probability of achieving an odd score?

d) What is the probability of scoring a multiple of 3?

e) What is the probability of scoring a multiple of 10?

f) What is the probability of scoring a factor of 60?

X	6	7	8	9
3				
4				
5				

Q3 A computer program randomly generates three letters of the alphabet with no duplication of letters. What is the probability that:

a) all three letters are vowels?

b) all three letters are consonants?

c) at least one of the three letters is a vowel?

Q4 A fair coin is tossed and a tetrahedral dice is rolled, with numbers 1, 2, 3 and 4 on its faces.

a) Compile a table showing all possible combinations.

b) Find the probability of getting

i) a head and a 2,

ii) a tail and a prime number,

iii) either a head or a 3 or both.

Questions on Tree Diagrams

Tree Diagrams are still Compound Probability, so you haven't really escaped. You'll be using what you know as well as new stuff — look at the example to see how it works.

A Likely Tree Diagram Question

I have a tub of sweets containing 4 lemon sherbets and 3 toffees. I take two sweets out at random. Using a tree diagram, find the probability of both sweets being toffees.

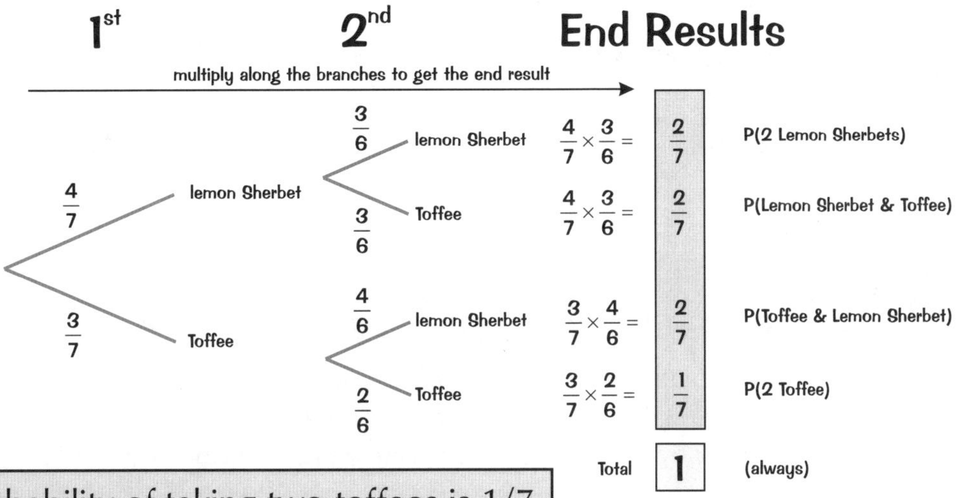

The probability of taking two toffees is 1/7.

Q1 Two marbles are taken from a box containing four red marbles, three green marbles and three white marbles. Draw a probability tree diagram to show this information. By using your tree diagram, find the probability that the two marbles taken from the box are the same colour.

Q2 A student needs to catch a bus and a train to get to university. The events and probabilities associated with each are shown on the tree diagram. For each event he can be late or on time. If he is late then he can catch the next bus or train. Work out the probability that:

a) the student catches the bus but misses the train

b) the student misses the bus but still manages to catch the train.

c) the student misses at least one mode of transport on his way to university.

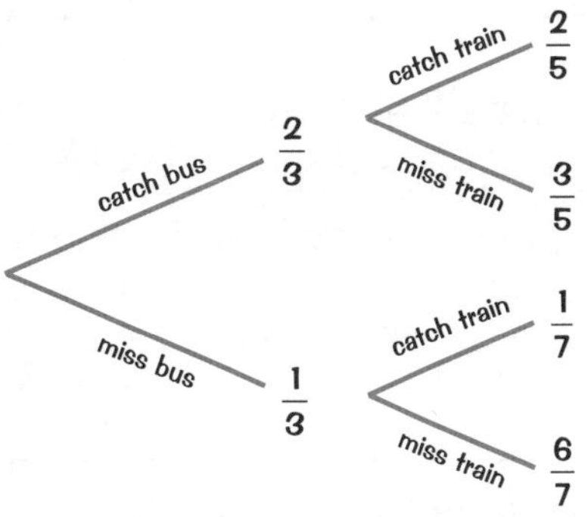

Q3 Two pool players, Sarah and Tina, play 3 games of pool in a match. Sarah is not as good as Tina. Sarah's chance of winning a game is 45%.

a) Draw a tree diagram to show the possible results of the 3 games.

b) What are the chances that Tina will win all 3 games?

c) As long as 1 player wins 2 or more games then they will win the actual match. What are the chances that Sarah will beat Tina over the 3 game match?

Questions on Scatter Graphs

Four facts about Correlation:

1) A SCATTER GRAPH is just a load of points on a graph that end up in a bit of a mess rather than in a nice line or curve.
2) There's a fancy word to say how much of a mess they're in — it's CORRELATION.
3) To draw a scatter graph, you just plot the points you are given on a graph.
4) There are different kinds of correlation, have a look at P.5 and P.6 of The Revision Guide for further details.

Q1 Match the following diagrams with the most appropriate descriptive label.

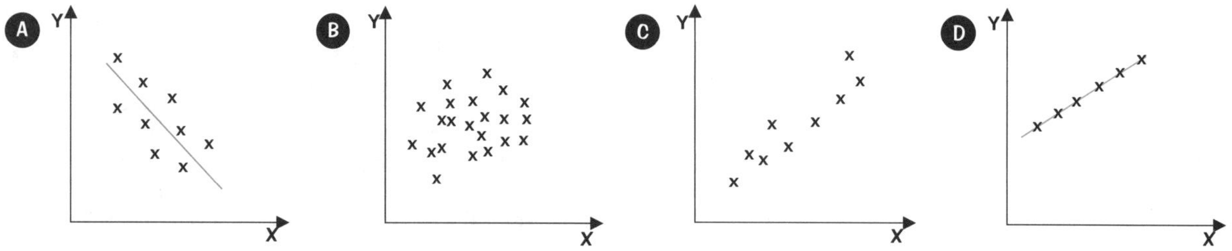

Labels:
- (P) Strong positive correlation
- (Q) Exact negative correlation
- (R) Little or no correlation
- (S) Moderate negative correlation
- (T) Medium correlation
- (U) Exact positive correlation

The most important thing with your line of best fit is to make sure you've got as many points on one side of the line as you've got on the other. Don't worry if there aren't that many points right on it, they're supposed to be a bit messy.

Q2 The table below shows the masses of 12 fathers and their eldest sons.

Mass of Father (kg)	65	71	67	69	67	63	62	70	66	68	68	64
Mass of son (kg)	68	70	67	68	68	66	66	68	65	71	69	65

a) Construct a scatter graph.
b) Draw a line of best fit.
c) Predict the weight of a son using your line of best fit, for a father who weighs 61 kg.

Q3 The bacterial count in a culture increases depending on the temperature the medium is kept at.

Bacterial Count (x 10^4)	7	8.1	9.2	10.0	11.1	12.4	13.2	14.3
Temperature (°C)	18	19	20	21	22	23	24	25

a) Construct a scatter graph and draw in a line of best fit.
b) From your line of best fit estimate:
i) what temperature will see a bacterial count of 100,000
ii) what bacterial count will be predicted for a temperature of 23.5°C.

Questions on Charts

Everyone loves a pie chart. Oh, no, sorry, that's pies.

When constructing a pie chart, follow the three steps:

1) Add up the numbers in each sector to get the TOTAL.
2) Divide 360° by the TOTAL to get the MULTIPLIER.
3) Multiply EVERY number by the MULTIPLIER to get the ANGLE of each SEGMENT.

Q1 A computerised attendance package is operated at a chicken plucking factory, to monitor absence and lateness. The list of absence or lateness is printed below for a particular week in January.

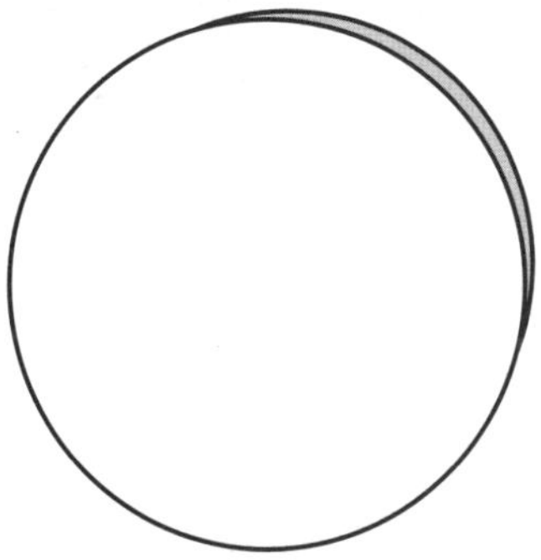

CHICKEN POX 4%	COLD 39%
BROKEN FINGERS 5%	OVERSLEPT 20%
DOCTOR'S APPOINTMENT 9%	FLU 23%

a) If these figures represent 200 absences or latenesses at the factory, how many people overslept?

b) Show this data on a pie chart, using the template on the left.

Q2 Mr Smith decides to sell his car and buy a motorbike. The pie chart illustrates his estimates for annual running costs.

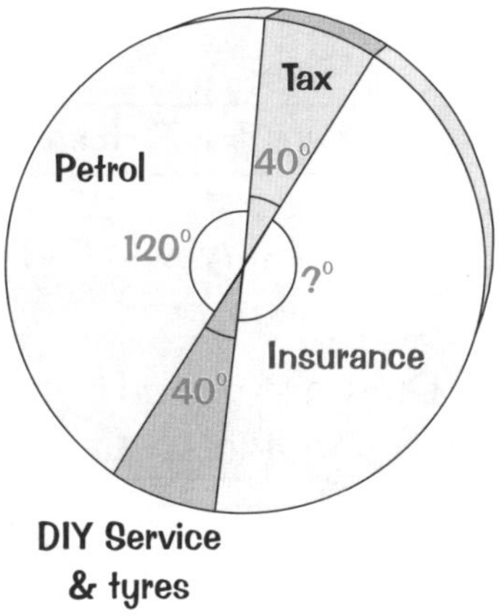

a) What is the missing angle?

b) If motorbike road tax is £50, calculate Mr Smith's estimates for:

i) DIY, service and tyres

ii) Insurance

iii) Petrol

iv) Total annual running costs

c) If all the costs were increased by 5% due to inflation, what angle should the insurance be?

Q3 One hundred people were asked in a survey what colour eyes they had. Use this two-way table to answer the following questions.

a) How many people in the survey had green eyes?

b) How many women took part in the survey?

c) How many women had blue eyes?

d) How many men had brown eyes?

	Green eyes	Blue eyes	Brown eyes	Total
Male	15			48
Female	20		23	
Total		21		100

Q4 Insects at a picnic were asked what their favourite food was. Use this two-way table to answer the following questions.

a) How many ants liked jam?

b) How many insects took part in the survey?

c) How many flies liked crisps?

	Cake	Crisps	Jam	Total
Ant	16	60		89
Fly			40	
Wasp	37		62	108
Total	90	95		

Questions on Stem and Leaf Diagrams

A stem and leaf diagram is a bit like a histogram, except there's no axes. The information is in the form of raw data. Just read off the numbers.

Q1 List the values shown in this stem and leaf diagram in ascending order.

0	3 3 3 5 8 8 9
1	2 3 4 4 8 8 9
2	0 2 2 4
3	1 3

Key: 1 | 4 means 14

Just to start you off, the first five values are: 3, 3, 3, 5, 8.

Q2 This stem and leaf diagram shows the marks in a test for a group of 25 students.

0	
10	0 2
20	0 1 4
30	0 2 3 3 3 7
40	1 1 3 6 7 9
50	1 2 6 8
60	1 4 9
70	9

Key: 1 | 3 means 13

Use the information in the diagram to answer these questions.

a) Find the number of students scoring 33.
b) Find the number of students scoring 40-49 inclusive.
c) Find the number of students scoring 55 or more:
d) Find the highest score.
e) Find the modal score.
f) Find the mean score.
g) Find the median score.

See P.8 of The Revision Guide for more on averages.

Q3 I did a survey to find out how many pets my friends have. Here are my results:

37	23	48	21	33	39
8	31	11	41	50	7
22	18	15	26	29	13

Draw a stem and leaf diagram to represent this data. Use this key:

Key: 1 | 4 means 14

Q4 Draw a stem and leaf diagram to represent the data below. Include a key.

101, 115, 122, 132, 126, 102, 124, 141, 139, 128,
123, 119, 131, 120, 125, 123, 117, 114, 130, 127

You don't have to have class widths of 10 — this diagram has class widths of 5. The numbers on the right are added to the ones on the left — so the key's slightly different.

		This means:
0	3	3
5	1 3 4	6, 8, 9
10	0 2 3	10, 12, 13
15	1	16

Key: 15 | 4 means 19

Q5 Represent the information in this bar chart using a stem and leaf diagram with class widths of 5.
I've done the first 4 bars for you:

0	2 2 3 3 3 4 4 4 4 4
5	0 0 0 0 0 0 0...
10	
15	
20	

Key: 15 | 4 means 19

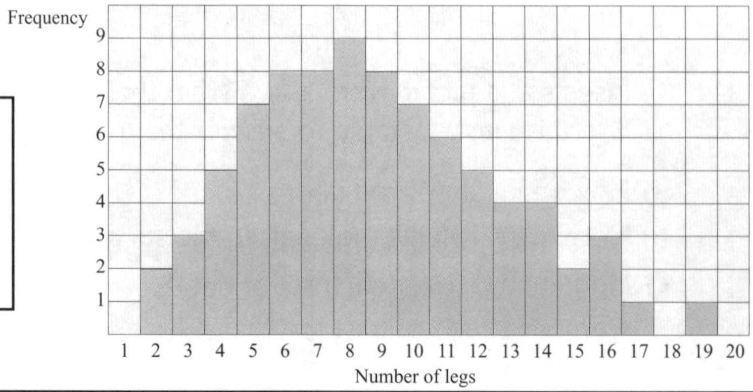

Questions on Averages and Range

In these questions, you only need to look at the numbers and work out the averages. There's loads of stuff in here that you really don't need, so ignore it.

Q1 The National Tree Service has collected data on two woods it manages. One in the North is Crookthwaite, and one in the South is Acornwood. The diameters of trees are calculated from their circumferences to the nearest centimetre.

diameter of trees	1 - 5	6 - 10	11 - 15	16 - 20	21 - 25	26 - 30	31 - 35	Total
Acornwood	1	5	8	20	4	1	1	40
Crookthwaite	6	4	5	4	7	3	1	30

a) Draw two frequency polygons to show this information.

b) What is the modal class interval for Acornwood?

c) What is the modal class interval for Crookthwaite?

d) Using your answers to the previous parts of the question, comment on the populations found in each of the woods, and compare the two.

Don't forget, put the data into ascending order before looking for the averages.

Q2 The population of a small hamlet reported the following household incomes:

£30,000	£22,000
£37,500	£27,500
£32,500	£25,000
£30,000	£40,000
£200,000	£35,000

a) Calculate the mean income of the population.

b) Calculate the mode and the median.

c) The mode and the median appear to agree very closely. Why is the mean so different?

d) Which measure would you quote as the "average" income for this small hamlet?

Q3 The Borders Orchid Growers Society has measured the height of all the Lesser Plumed Bog Orchids in the 5 mile wide strip each side of the border, to the nearest cm.

5 miles on Scottish side

Heights 14, 15, 17, 14, 17, 16, 14, 13
15, 17, 16, 14, 15, 17, 14, 13

5 miles on English side

Heights 14, 12, 16, 18, 19, 17, 16, 15
13, 14, 15, 16, 17, 18, 19, 13

a) Draw a tally chart for each set of data the Borders Orchid Growers Society has collected.

b) Draw a bar chart for each set of data.

c) State the mode and median for each set of data.

d) Find the range for each set of data.

e) Compare and contrast the two sides of the border using the data you have compiled.

If you've learnt anything about fat trees or bog orchids you've missed my point.

Questions on Time Series

Q1 Which of the following sets of measurements form time series?

a) The average rainfall in Cumbria, measured each day for a year.

b) The daily rainfall in European capital cities on Christmas Day, 2000.

c) The shoe size of everybody in Class 6C on September 1st, 2001.

d) My shoe size (measured every month) from when I was twelve months old to when I was fourteen years old.

Q2 **a)** Which two of the following time series are seasonal, and which two are not seasonal?

A

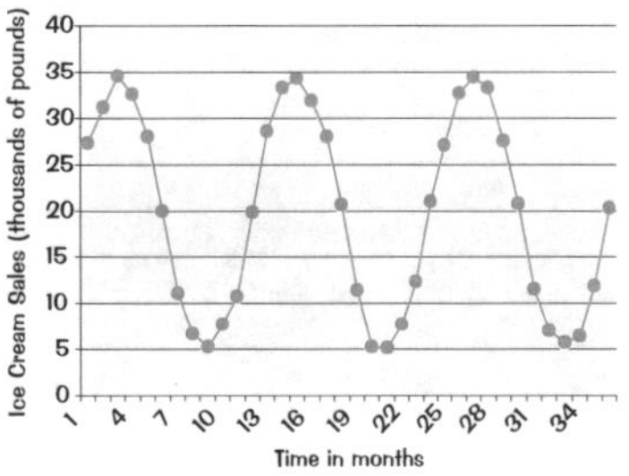

B

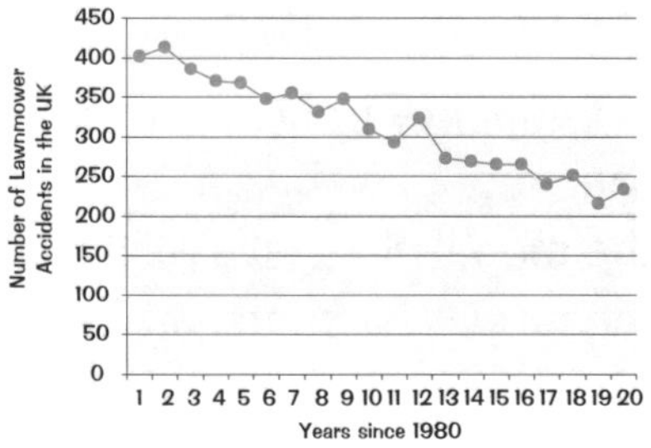

C

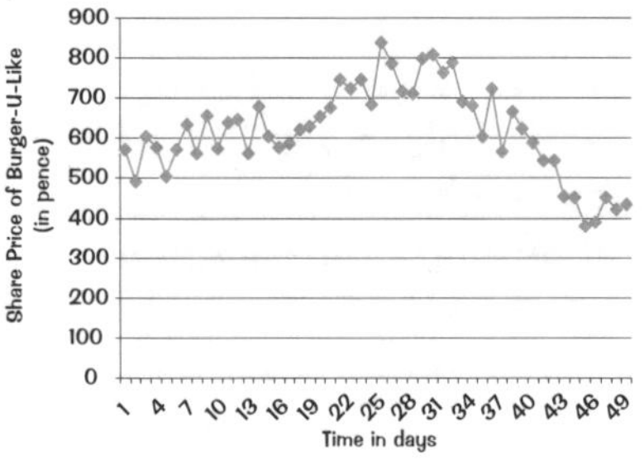

D

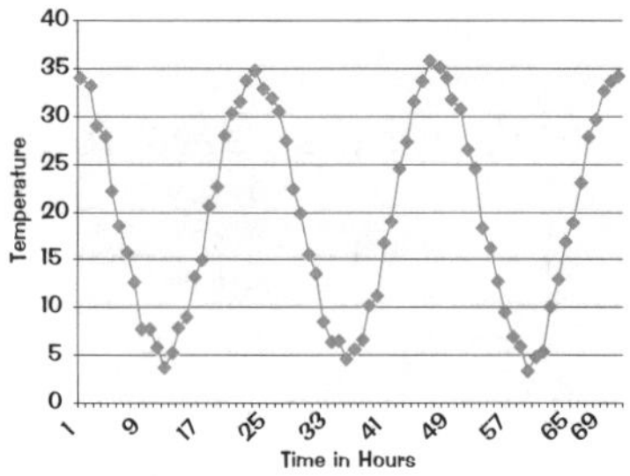

b) What are the periods of the time series which are seasonal?

c) Describe the trends in the time series which are **not** seasonal.

Q3 The following table shows the value of a knitwear company's sock sales in the years 1998-2000. The sales figures are given in thousands of pounds.

Time	Sales
Spring 1998	404
Summer 1998	401
Autumn 1998	411
Winter 1998	420
Spring 1999	416
Summer 1999	409
Autumn 1999	419
Winter 1999	424
Spring 2000	416
Summer 2000	413
Autumn 2000	427
Winter 2000	440

a) Plot the figures on a graph with time on the horizontal axis and sales on the vertical axis.

b) Calculate a 4-point moving average to smooth the series. Write your answers in the boxes provided.

c) Plot the moving average on the same axes as your original graph.

d) Describe the trend of the sales figures.

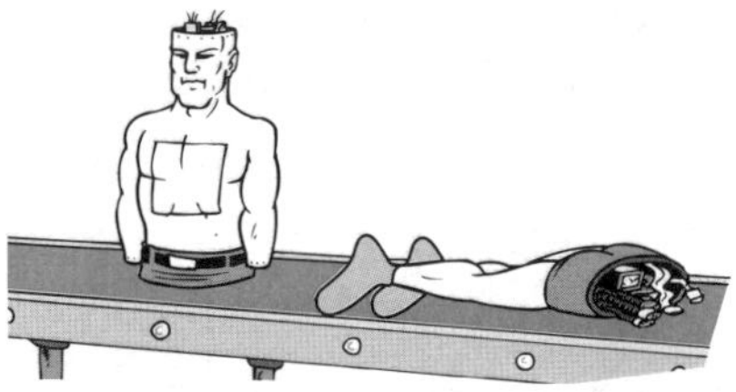

Questions on Frequency Tables

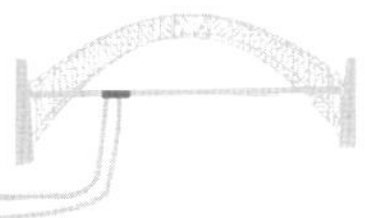

Frequency Tables look quite tricky, so you'd better make sure you know how they work.

Frequency Tables contain three rows:

1) The 1st row (or column) gives us the Group Labels, eg weights of 50 kg, 55 kg, etc.
2) The 2nd row (or column) is the actual frequency data, eg 10 people weigh 50 kg, etc.
3) The 3rd row (or column) is just the other two multiplied together and is left for you to fill in.

Q1 120 male pupils were weighed to the nearest kg. Calculate:

a) the median weight

b) the modal weight

c) the mean weight, by first completing the table.

Mass (kg)	Frequency	Mass x Freq.
61	22	
62	44	
63	35	
64	19	

Q2 20 pupils are asked to estimate the length, to the nearest cm, of their teacher's table. Put the estimates in the frequency table below:

148 142 140 138 136 136 132 128 126 128
146 144 138 140 138 134 138 128 124 124

Estimate	124	126	128	130	132	134	136	138	140	142	144	146	148
Frequency													

a) Find the mode. **b)** Find the median. **c)** State the range.

Q3 The total weight of 15 rugby players is 1350 kg.
The total weight of 9 ballet dancers is 360 kg.
What is the mean weight of the group of 24 people when put together?

Q4 A dentist is about to employ a dental hygienist. She wishes to know if having a dental hygienist has an effect on the number of fillings she has to perform each year. So, prior to appointing him, the dentist takes some data from the record cards. Here it is:

No. of fillings	0	1	2	3	4	5
No. of children	1	2	8	30	60	12

Three years after appointing the dental hygienist, the dentist takes another set of data from the record cards. Here it is:

No. of fillings	0	1	2	3	4	5
No. of children	11	16	40	32	4	2

Using any statistical average you need, state what you see from the data, assuming that these records are for new patients.

Questions on Cumulative Frequency

As a rule these are trickier than standard frequency tables — you'll certainly have to tread carefully here. Have a good look at the box below and make sure you remember it.

Mean and Mid-Interval Values

1) The MID-INTERVAL VALUES are just what they sound like – the middle of the group.
2) Using the Frequencies and Mid-Interval Values you can work out the MEAN.

$$\text{Mean} = \frac{\text{Overall Total (Frequency} \times \text{Mid-Interval Value)}}{\text{Frequency Total}}$$

Shoe Size	1 - 2	3 - 4	5 - 6	7 - 8	Totals
Frequency	15	10	3	1	29
Mid-Interval Value	1.5	3.5	5.5	7.5	—
Frequency x Mid-Interval Value	22.5	35	16.5	7.5	81.5

So the Mean value is 81.5 ÷ 29 = 2.81

Q1 In a survey of test results in a French class at Blugdon High, these grades were achieved by the 23 pupils:

a) Write down the Mid-Interval Values for each of the groups.
b) Calculate the Mean value.

(grade) score	(E) 31-40	(D) 41-50	(C) 51-60	(B) 61-70
frequency	4	7	8	4

Q2 The table below shows donations to a sponsored walk.

Sponsored Walk Donations	1p - 10p	11p - 20p	21p - 30p	31p - 40p	41p - 50p
Frequency	10	13	16	15	12
Cumulative Frequency	10	23			

Cumulative frequency just means a running total of the frequency data.

a) Complete the table by filling in the cumulative frequency.
b) Calculate the Mean value.

Q3 This table shows times for each team of swimmers, the Dolphins and the Sharks.

Dolphins			Sharks		
Time interval (seconds)	Frequency	Mid-interval value	Time interval (seconds)	Frequency	Mid-interval value
14-19	3	16.5	14-19	6	16.5
20-25	7	22.5	20-25	15	22.5
26-31	15		26-31	33	
32-37	32		32-37	59	
38-43	45		38-43	20	
44-49	30		44-49	8	
50-55	5		50-55	2	

a) Complete the table, writing in all mid-interval values.
b) Use the mid-interval technique to estimate the mean time for each team.

Questions on Box Plots

From the Cumulative Frequency Curve you can get 3 vital statistics:

1) MEDIAN
2) LOWER / UPPER QUARTILES
3) INTERQUARTILE RANGE

From the graph:
MEDIAN = 40 kg
LOWER QUARTILE = 30 kg
UPPER QUARTILE = 60 kg
INTER-QUARTILE RANGE = 60 kg–30 kg
= 30 kg

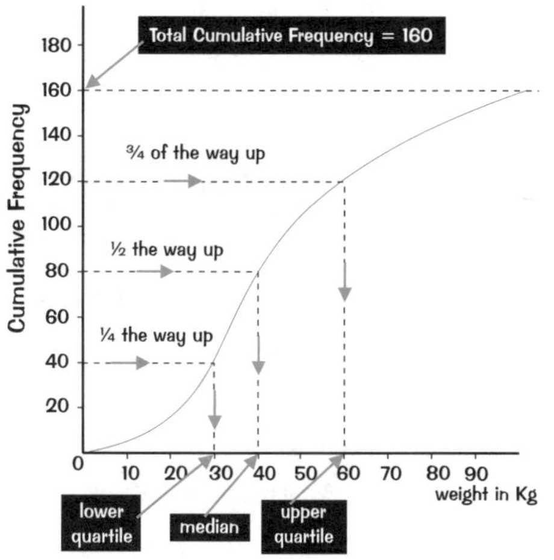

Q1 This table shows the number of wickets taken by 80 bowlers in cricket matches over the course of a season.

a) Draw a cumulative frequency diagram from this data.

b) Use it to estimate the median.

c) What is the interquartile range of the data?

No. of Wickets	1 - 10	11 - 20	21 - 30	31 - 40	41 - 50	51 - 60	61 - 70	71 - 80	81 - 90	91 - 100
No. of Bowlers	2	3	5	7	19	16	14	10	3	1
Cumulative Freq.										

To draw a box plot:

1) Use the same scale as the c.f. curve.

2) Draw lines down from the median, upper and lower quartiles, and maximum and minimum lines.

3) Draw a box between the upper and lower quartiles, and divide it in two by drawing a line down the box for the median. Then finish it off with horizontal lines (or "whiskers") from the box to the maximum/minimum points.

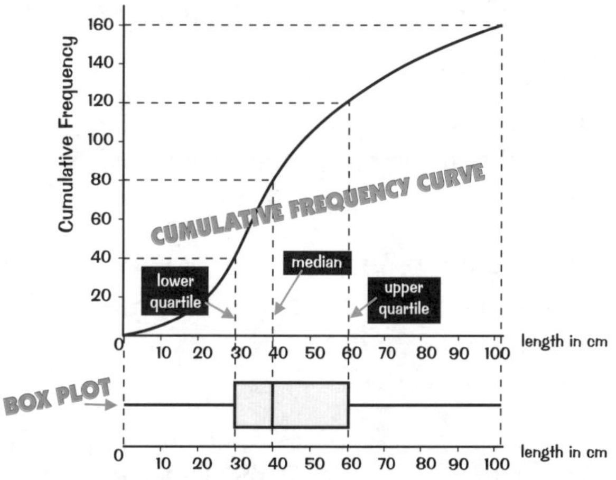

Q2 Egbert noted the attention span of several of his friends, while talking to them about the fall of communism in Eastern Europe. The results, in seconds, were as follows:

33 23 31 33 37 42 27 42 36 34 30 25 43 39 38
49 33 38 47 36 21 31 28 34 31 36 30 39 32 33

a) Put the data into this frequency table.

Attention Span (seconds)	20 – 24	25 – 29	30 – 34	35 – 39	40 – 44	45 – 49
Frequency						
Cumulative Frequency						

b) Construct the cumulative frequency curve.

c) Draw the box plot underneath the cumulative frequency curve.

Complete this phrase:
"I wandered lonely as a..."

A: penguin C: poet
B: cloud D: fish

Questions on Prime Numbers

Basically, prime numbers don't divide by anything — and actually that's the best way to think of them. Have a go at the questions and you'll see what I mean.

1) Prime Numbers are all the numbers that don't come up in times tables.
2) The only way to get any Prime Number is 1 × ITSELF.
3) For example, the only numbers that multiply to give 5 are 1×5.

Q1 Using any or all of the figures 1, 2, 3, 7 write down:

a) the smallest prime number
b) a prime number greater than 20
c) a prime number between 10 and 20
d) two prime numbers whose sum is 20
e) a number that is not prime.

Don't forget that number one is not a prime — simple as that.

Q2 Write down the first ten prime numbers.

Q3 Find all the prime numbers between 40 and 50.

Q4 In the ten by ten square opposite, ring all the prime numbers. (The first three have been done for you.)

1	2	3	4	5	6	7	8	9	10
11	12	13	14	15	16	17	18	19	20
21	22	23	24	25	26	27	28	29	30
31	32	33	34	35	36	37	38	39	40
41	42	43	44	45	46	47	48	49	50
51	52	53	54	55	56	57	58	59	60
61	62	63	64	65	66	67	68	69	70
71	72	73	74	75	76	77	78	79	80
81	82	83	84	85	86	87	88	89	90
91	92	93	94	95	96	97	98	99	100

Q5 Among the prime numbers between 10 and 100, find three which are still prime when their digits are reversed.

This stuff keeps coming up in the Exam — so make sure you can check if a number's prime or not. This is actually dead easy — have a look at the simple method on P.15 of The Revision Guide.

Q6 What is the largest prime less than 500?

Q7 Give a reason for 27 not being a prime number.

Q8 How many prime numbers are even?

Q9 A school ran three evening classes: judo, karate and kendo. The judo class had 29 pupils, the karate class had 27 and the kendo class 23. For which classes did the teacher have difficulty dividing the pupils into equal groups?

Q10 Find a set of three prime numbers which adds up to each of the following numbers:
10 29 41

Questions on Multiples and Factors

This is real basic stuff — you just have to know your times tables. The only tricky bit is remembering which is a multiple and which is a factor — so learn the definitions and you won't go far wrong.

The <u>MULTIPLES</u> of a number are simply its <u>TIMES TABLE</u>		The <u>FACTORS</u> of a number are all the numbers that <u>DIVIDE INTO IT</u>.
eg The lowest three multiples of 3 are:	*<u>3</u> because 3 = 3 x 1* *<u>6</u> because 6 = 3 x 2* *<u>9</u> because 9 = 3 x 3*	*eg <u>12</u> can be made by: <u>1×12</u> or <u>2×6</u> or <u>3×4</u>* *so the <u>factors of 12</u> are <u>1, 2, 3, 4, 6, 12</u>.*

Q1 From the numbers 1, 3, 4, 5, 6, 9, 10, 17, 23, 26, 27, 36 and 42, write down:
a) all the <u>prime numbers</u>
b) all the <u>multiples</u> of 6
c) all the factors of 48.

Q2 List <u>all</u> the factors of the following numbers: **a)** 63 **b)** 80 **c)** 120 **d)** 220

Q3 Express each of the following as the sum of <u>two prime numbers</u>: **a)** 10 **b)** 20 **c)** 30

Q4 Which of the following: 1, 2, 3, 4, 7, 8, 9, 12, 15, 23, 24, 36
a) are multiples of 3?
b) are prime numbers?

Basically, prime factors are just factors which are prime numbers — nice and easy, this bit.

Q5 Express the following as a <u>product of prime factors</u>:
a) 7 **c)** 47 **e)** 648 **g)** 405
b) 9 **d)** 105 **f)** 210 **h)** 25920

Q6 **a)** Write 1575 as a product of its <u>prime factors</u>.
b) If $315 = 3^x \times 5^y \times 7^z$, find x, y and z.

Q7 The prime factorisation of a certain number is $2^3 \times 7 \times 13$.
a) What is the number?
b) What is the prime factorisation of 1/2 of this number?
c) What is the prime factorisation of 1/4 of this number?
d) What is the prime factorisation of 1/8 of this number?

The thing to remember is to always multiply out your answer — if you don't get back to the number you started with you've definitely missed a factor, so try again.

Q8 A packing carton measures 36 cm by 42 cm by 48 cm. The carton is filled with <u>cube</u> shaped boxes of chocolates, with no air gaps.
a) How big can the boxes of chocolates be?
b) How many boxes of chocolates, of the size worked out in **a**), will fit in the carton?

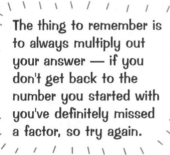

Q9 George bought 3 identical lengths of ribbon.
He cut the first into an exact number of 2 cm lengths, the second into an exact number of 12 cm lengths and the third into an exact number of 15 cm lengths.

What is the smallest length that the ribbons could have been?

Questions on LCM and HCF

These two fancy names always put people off — but really they're dead easy. Just learn these simple facts:

1) The Lowest Common Multiple (LCM) is the SMALLEST number that will DIVIDE BY ALL the numbers in question.

eg 3, 6, 9, 12, 15 are all multiples of 3
5, 10, 15, 20, 25 are all multiples of 5
The lowest number that is in both lists is 15, so 15 is the LCM of 3 and 5.

2) The Highest Common Factor (HCF) is the BIGGEST number that will DIVIDE INTO ALL the numbers in question.

eg 1, 2, 4, 8 are all factors of 8
1, 2, 3, 4, 6, 12 are all factors of 12
The highest number that is in both lists is 4, so 4 is the HCF of 8 and 12.

Q1 **a)** List the first ten multiples of 6, starting at 6.
b) List the first ten multiples of 5, starting at 5.
c) What is the LCM of 5 and 6?

I tell you what, it's a lot easier to find the LCM or HCF once you've listed the factors or multiples. If you miss out this step it'll all go horribly wrong, believe me.

Q2 **a)** List all the factors of 30.
b) List all the factors of 48.
c) What is the HCF of 30 and 48?

Q3 For each set of numbers, find the HCF.

a) 3, 5 **b)** 6, 8 **c)** 10, 15 **d)** 27, 48 **e)** 14, 21 **f)** 16, 32 **g)** 52, 72 **h)** 11, 33, 121

Q4 For each set of numbers, find the LCM.

a) 3, 5 **b)** 6, 8 **c)** 10, 15 **d)** 15, 18 **e)** 14, 21 **f)** 16, 32 **g)** 6, 15 **h)** 11, 33, 44

Q5 Lars, Rita and Alan regularly go swimming. Lars goes every 2 days, Rita goes every 3 days and Alan goes every 5 days. They all went swimming together on Friday 1st June.
a) On what date will Lars and Rita next go swimming together?
b) On what date will Rita and Alan next go swimming together?
c) On what day of the week will all 3 next go swimming together?
d) Which of the 3 (if any) will go swimming on 15th June?

Q6 For each set of numbers, find the HCF.

a) 40, 60 **b)** 10, 40, 60 **c)** 10, 24, 40, 60 **d)** 15, 45 **e)** 15, 30, 45 **f)** 15, 20, 30, 45 **g)** 32, 64 **h)** 32, 48, 64 **i)** 16, 32, 48, 64

Q7 For each set of numbers, find the LCM.

a) 40, 60 **b)** 10, 40, 60 **c)** 10, 24, 40, 60 **d)** 15, 45 **e)** 15, 30, 45 **f)** 15, 20, 30, 45 **g)** 32, 64 **h)** 32, 48, 64 **i)** 16, 32, 48, 64

Questions on Powers (Indices)

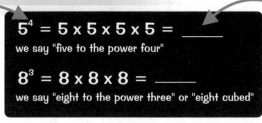

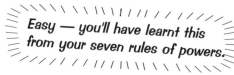

Hang on there. Before you try this page, make sure you know the seven rules for powers — you'll find them on P.18 of The Revision Guide, or you could just ask Teach.

The small number is called the <u>power</u> or <u>index number.</u> Remember the plural of index is <u>indices.</u>

$5^4 = 5 \times 5 \times 5 \times 5 =$ ____
we say "five to the power four"

$8^3 = 8 \times 8 \times 8 =$ ____
we say "eight to the power three" or "eight cubed"

To save time try using the power button on your calculator x^y y^x

eg. 5 x^y 4 =

8 x^y 3 =

Q1 Complete the following:

a) $2^4 = 2 \times 2 \times 2 \times 2 =$

b) $10^3 = 10 \times 10 \times 10 =$

c) $4^6 = 4\times \qquad =$

d) $1^9 = 1\times \qquad =$

Q2 Simplify the following:

a) $2 \times 2 \times 2 \times 2 \times 2 \times 2 \times 2 \times 2$

b) $12 \times 12 \times 12 \times 12 \times 12$

c) $m \times m \times m$

d) $y \times y \times y \times y$

Q3 Complete the following:

a) $10^2 \times 10^3 = \qquad = 10^5$

b) $10^3 \times 10^4 = \qquad =$

c) $10^4 \times 10^2 = \qquad =$

Easy — you'll have learnt this from your seven rules of powers.

Q4 Complete:

a) $4^5 \div 4^3 = \dfrac{(4 \times 4 \times 4 \times 4 \times 4)}{\qquad} =$

b) $8^5 \div 8^2 = \qquad =$

Q5 Which of the following are <u>true</u>?

a) $2^4 \times 2^6 = 2^{10}$

b) $2^2 \times 2^3 \times 2^4 = 2^9$

c) $4^{10} \times 4^4 \times 4^2 = 4^{18}$

d) $2^1 \times 2^3 \times 2^4 = 2^8$

e) $2^{20} \div 2^5 = 2^4$

f) $3^{12} \div 3^4 = 3^8$

g) $10^{20} \div 10^3 = 10^{17}$

h) $4^6 \div (4^2 \times 4^3) = 4^1$

Q6 Write the following as a <u>single term</u>:

a) $10^6 \div 10^4$

b) $(8^2 \times 8^5) \div 8^3$

c) $a^5 \times a^4$

d) $p^4 \times p^5 \times p^6$

e) $x^3 \div x^2$

f) $h^{12} \div (h^4 \times h^4)$

Q7 Use your <u>calculator</u> to find the exact value of

a) 4^3

b) 3^5

c) 10^4

d) 4^1

e) 12^5

f) 5^{-1}

g) 10^{-2}

h) 50^{-1}

i) 2^{-3}

j) 10^{-5}

Q8 Write as a <u>single power</u>:

a) $(x^2)^4$

b) $(y^6)^2$

c) $(z^{10})^2$

d) $(x^2)^{-3}$

e) $(y^{-1})^6$

Q9 Find the numbers replaced by x in these statements:

a) $3^x = 9$

b) $3^x = 1/9$

c) $10^x = 1000$

d) $4^x = 1/16$

e) $17^x = 1$

f) $3^x \times 3^{-1} = 3^5$

g) $(4^2)^x = 4^6$

h) $(5^x)^2 = 5^6$

i) $8^x = 1/8$

j) $x^5 = 1$

Questions on Squares and Cubes

Q1 Work out without a calculator:

a) 5^2 = ... **b)** 7^2 = ... **c)** 2^3 = ... **d)** 4^3 = ...

e) 6^2 = ... **f)** 5^3 = ... **g)** 9^2 = ... **h)** 10^3 = ...

Q2 Do these with a calculator:

a) 1.4^2 = ... **b)** 3.5^2 = ... **c)** 5.95^2 = ... **d)** 7.63^3 = ...

e) $3^2 + 6^2$ = ... **f)** $7^3 - 5^3$ = ... **g)** $6^3 - 14^2$ = ...

Q3 Put a ring round the square numbers in the following list:

17 6 9 15 4 16 21 11 20 1 50

Q4 Put a ring round the cube numbers in the following list:

8 25 27 1 100 125 42 10 16 30 18

Q5 Work out:

a) 10 squared = ... **b)** 4 cubed = ...

Q6 What is the next square number after 64? ....

Q7 What is the next cube number after 216? ....

Q8 Work out with or without a calculator:

a) $2^3 \times 5^2$ = ... **b)** $3^2 \times 1^3$ = ... **c)** $3^3 \times 2^2$ = ...

Q9 Write down two square numbers which are also cube numbers.

Q10 A block of flats with 20 floors has 20 windows on each floor.
How many windows does the building have altogether?
If it takes 20 minutes to clean each window, how many minutes does it take to clean the block?

....

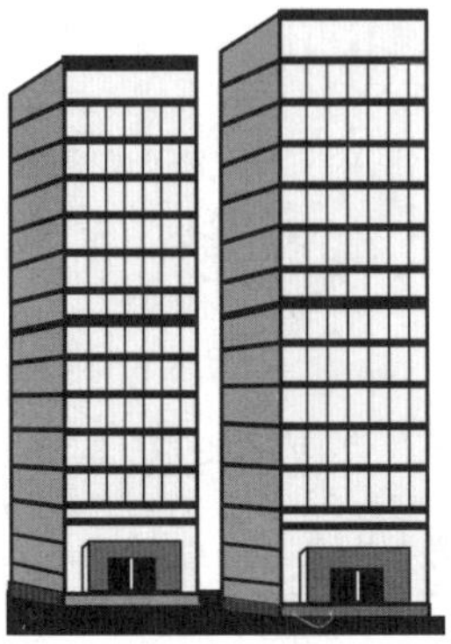

These aren't as bad as they seem — "three squared" = $3^2 = 3 \times 3 = 9$. Same with cubes — "ten cubed" = $10^3 = 10 \times 10 \times 10 = 1000$.

Questions on Square and Cube Roots

"Square Root" means "What Number Times by Itself gives..."

Eg. The square roots of 64 are 8 and –8, the square roots of 36 are 6 and –6 etc.

That's because 8 × 8 = 64 and (–8) × (–8) = 64... OK, I was just checking.

Q1 Write down both answers for each of the following:

a) $\sqrt{4}$ **d)** $\sqrt{49}$ **g)** $\sqrt{144}$

b) $\sqrt{16}$ **e)** $\sqrt{25}$ **h)** $\sqrt{64}$

c) $\sqrt{9}$ **f)** $\sqrt{100}$ **i)** $\sqrt{81}$

Q2 Use the $\sqrt{\ }$ button on your calculator to find the following positive square roots to the nearest whole number.

a) $\sqrt{60}$ **e)** $\sqrt{520}$ **i)** $\sqrt{170}$

b) $\sqrt{19}$ **f)** $\sqrt{75}$ **j)** $\sqrt{7220}$

c) $\sqrt{34}$ **g)** $\sqrt{750}$ **k)** $\sqrt{1000050}$

d) $\sqrt{200}$ **h)** $\sqrt{0.9}$ **l)** $\sqrt{27}$

Q3 Use your calculator to find, to 1dp, the following square roots (two answers for each):

a) $45^{\frac{1}{2}}$ **b)** $18^{\frac{1}{2}}$ **c)** $90^{\frac{1}{2}}$

Remember, the power ½ means a square root.

Q4 Without using your calculator, try to predict the following positive square roots to the nearest whole number. (Your answers to **Q1** will be helpful.)

a) $\sqrt{10}$ **c)** $\sqrt{80}$

b) $\sqrt{50}$ **d)** $\sqrt{65}$

Check your answers using a calculator afterwards.

Q5 A square rug has an area of 235.3156 m². What is the length of an edge?

Q6 A square bowling green has an area of 2025 m². What is the perimeter of the green?

"Cube Root" means "What Number Times by Itself Twice gives..."

Eg. The cube root of 64 is 4, the cube root of 27 is 3 etc.

4 × 4 × 4 = 64, 3 × 3 × 3 = 27 — you get the picture...

Q7 Use your calculator to find the following:

a) $\sqrt[3]{125}$ **d)** $\sqrt[3]{729}$ **g)** $\sqrt[3]{1}$ **j)** $\sqrt[3]{343}$

b) $\sqrt[3]{1728}$ **e)** $\sqrt[3]{1331}$ **h)** $\sqrt[3]{0.125}$ **k)** $\sqrt[3]{4096}$

c) $\sqrt[3]{1000}$ **f)** $\sqrt[3]{8000}$ **i)** $\sqrt[3]{216}$ **l)** $\sqrt[3]{1000000}$

Q8 Without using your calculator, try to predict the following to the nearest whole number.

a) $\sqrt[3]{120}$ **c)** $\sqrt[3]{200}$ **e)** $\sqrt[3]{300}$

b) $\sqrt[3]{1800}$ **d)** $\sqrt[3]{4000}$

Same again — check your answers with a calculator.

Questions on Multiplying and Dividing

Don't forget to put a zero under the units when you multiply by that extra number in the tens column.

Q1 Multiply the following without a calculator:

a) 23 × 10
b) 13 × 1000
c) 17 × 100
d) 98 × 1,000,000
e) 4 × 30
f) 25 × 20
g) 15 × 300
h) 8 × 2000
i) 3.3 × 100
j) 7.1 × 1,000,000
k) 0.539 × 10
l) 4.4 × 10,000
m) 5.3 × 40
n) 4.5 × 300
o) 0.5 × 200

Q2 What is the total cost (in pounds) of:

a) 6 pens at 50p each
b) 7 computers at £600 each
c) 17 bikes at £100 each
d) 23 bananas at 20p each
e) 400 tins of custard at 80p each
f) 1,000,000 bars of chocolate at 30p each
g) 50 pairs of large yellow pants at £2.50 each
h) 1000 tubes of toothpaste at 58p each

Q3 Do these divisions without a calculator:

a) 35 ÷ 100
b) 480 ÷ 10
c) 1700 ÷ 1,000
d) 918 ÷ 10,000
e) 6 ÷ 20
f) 84 ÷400
g) 9900 ÷ 300
h) 64,400 ÷ 2,000
i) 6.7 ÷ 10
j) 0.1 ÷ 1,000
k) 3.14 ÷ 100
l) 5,555,000 ÷ 10,000
m) 16 ÷ 40
n) 660 ÷ 200
o) 255 ÷ 5,000

Q4 Seven people share a lottery win of £868.00.
How much does each person get?

Q5 A chocolate cake containing 944 calories is split into 8 equal slices.
How many calories are in each slice?

Questions on Negative Numbers

Negative numbers are pretty easy when you're used to them. Start by drawing yourself a number line, then count along it. After you've done a few questions, you'll find you can work them out in your head.

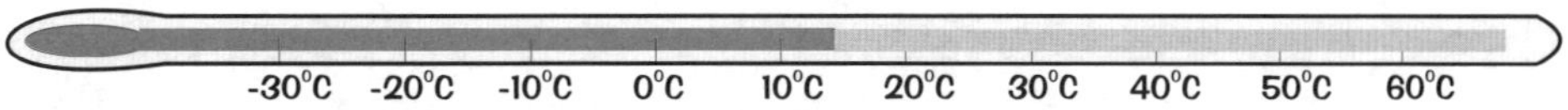

(This first one's given you a thermometer, which has got its own number line, anyway.)

Q1 Work out the temperature rise for each of the following:

a) 10°C to 42°C **c)** -4°C to 42°C **e)** -30°C to -25°C
b) -10°C to 0°C **d)** -29°C to 4°C **f)** -18°C to 4°C

Q2 Work out the drop in temperature for each of the following:

a) 30°C to -10°C **c)** 40°C to -30°C **e)** 50°C to -30°C
b) 24°C to -4°C **d)** -10°C to -25°C **f)** -3°C to -5°C

Q3 The temperature at midday was 18°C. By evening it had fallen by 23°C. What was the evening temperature?

Q4 What is the difference in height between the following points?

a) H and T **d)** W and T
b) R and H **e)** H and W
c) W and R **f)** T and R

Hint: take the sea level as zero, then do a number line up the side.

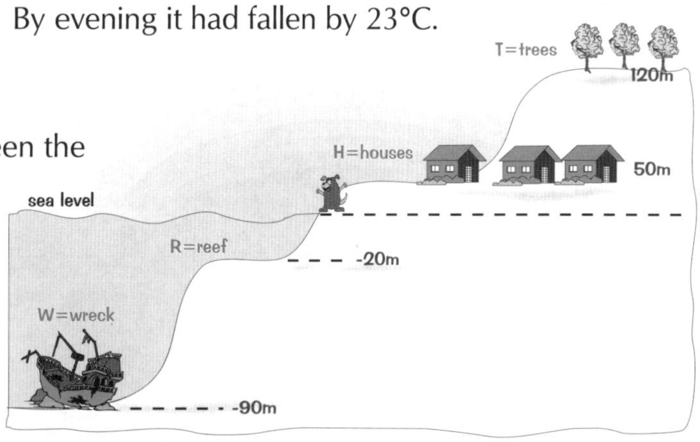

Q5 Find the value of each of the following:

a) 13 – 5 **c)** -2 + 2 **e)** -3 – 4 **g)** -1 + 2 – (-4)
b) 6 – 7 **d)** -10 + 5 **f)** -20 – (-100) **h)** 1 – (-2) + 4

Q6 Work out the following:

a) -4 × -3 **d)** -8 ÷ 4 **g)** 2 × -2
b) 5 × -2 **e)** -20 ÷ -10 **h)** -36 ÷ -12
c) -12 ÷ -4 **f)** -4 × 4 **i)** -40 × 3

Rules for Multiplying and Dividing

× or ÷	+ ve	– ve
+ ve	+	–
– ve	–	+

Multiply / divide the numbers ignoring the signs first, then put in the +/– signs afterwards, using that rule you've just learnt.

Q7 Find the value of xy and x/y for the following:

a) x = 20, y = 4 **c)** x = 40, y = -4
b) x = 36, y = -2 **d)** x = 18, y = -3

Q8 Which is larger and by how much:

a) (5 + 2) × (7 – 4) or **b)** 5 + 2(7 – 4) ?

Q9 Find the value of (a – b) ÷ c when a = -2, b = 10 and c = -4.

Questions on Fractions and Decimals

Remember, decimals are just a simple way of writing fractions — so it's easy to convert between the two. It's even easier if you get your calculator to do the hard work — so use it.

To convert decimals to fractions, write the number as a fraction of 10, 100 etc, then cancel down.	To convert fractions to decimals just use your calculator and divide.
Eg: $0.6 = \frac{6}{10} = \frac{3}{5}$ $0.15 = \frac{15}{100} = \frac{3}{20}$ $0.025 = \frac{25}{1000} = \frac{1}{40}$	Eg: $\frac{2}{3} = 2 \div 3 = 0.667$ $\frac{75}{100} = 75 \div 100 = 0.75$ $\frac{120}{150} = 120 \div 150 = 0.8$

Q1 Write the following fractions as decimals, giving your answer to 4 d.p.

a) $\frac{1}{2}$ **e)** $\frac{1}{16}$ **i)** $\frac{6}{7}$ **m)** $\frac{42}{51}$

b) $\frac{1}{4}$ **f)** $\frac{1}{25}$ **j)** $\frac{8}{15}$ **n)** $\frac{17}{19}$

c) $\frac{1}{10}$ **g)** $\frac{3}{4}$ **k)** $\frac{4}{21}$ **o)** $\frac{1}{11}$

d) $\frac{1}{20}$ **h)** $\frac{19}{20}$ **l)** $\frac{7}{18}$ **p)** $\frac{0}{100}$

Q2 Write the following decimals as fractions:

a) 0.1 **e)** 0.19 **i)** 0.25 **m)**0.125

b) 0.2 **f)** 0.473 **j)** 0.3 **n)** 0.72

c) 0.34 **g)** 0.101 **k)** 0.4 **o)** 0.8764

d) 0.9 **h)** 0.16 **l)** 0.86 **p)** 1.2

Sometimes they put in extra details to confuse you. Just ignore it — simply write down the fraction or decimal then carry out the conversion. Go on, outsmart them.

Q3 During the football season, Chris collected 0.45 of his favourite team's stickers. Write this decimal as a fraction.

Q4 Fill in the gaps in the conversion table on the right:

FRACTION	DECIMAL
$^1/_{10}$	
	0.15
	0.9
$^1/_8$	
$^3/_{16}$	
	0.375
$^9/_{20}$	
	0.625
$^9/_8$	

Q5 Over the course of a formula one motor race, 8/22 of the cars did not finish. Write this fraction as a decimal.

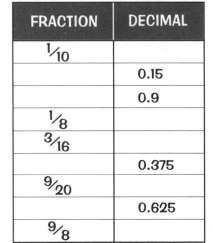

Questions on Decimals and Percentages

I reckon that converting decimals to percentages is about as easy as it gets — so make the most of it.

All you're doing is multiplying by 100 — it really couldn't be easier.

DECIMALS TO PERCENTAGES	
Move the decimal point 2 places to the right.	Eg 0.5 = 50% 0.62 = 62% 0.359 = 35.9%

Q1 Express each of the following as a percentage:

a) 0.25 **c)** 1.0 **e)** 0.221 **g)** 0.4152

b) 0.5 **d)** 0.2 **f)** 0.546 **h)** 0.8406

PERCENTAGES TO DECIMALS	
Move the decimal point 2 places to the left.	Eg 20% = 0.2 75% = 0.75 33.3% = 0.333

Now you're dividing by 100 — so just move the decimal point the other way. It's as simple as that.

Q2 Express each percentage as a decimal:

a) 50% **d)** 62% **g)** 60.2%

b) 12% **e)** 17% **h)** 54.9%

c) 40% **f)** 16% **i)** 75.16%

Q3 Harold estimates that 0.24 of his collection of racing snails are from Great Britain and Northern Ireland. Write this decimal as a percentage.

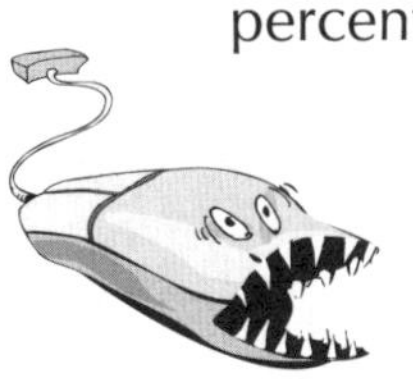

Express 1/5 as a percentage	Express 60% as a fraction
1) Fraction to Decimal: 1 ÷ 5 = 0.2 2) Decimal to Percentage: (move the decimal point) 20%	1) Percentage to Decimal: (move the decimal point) 0.6 2) Decimal to Fraction: 6/10 = 3/5

Q4 Express each percentage as a fraction in its lowest terms:

a) 25% **c)** 51% **e)** 98% **g)** 8.2%

b) 60% **d)** 20% **f)** 8% **h)** 49.6%

Q5 Express each of the following as a percentage:

a) $\frac{1}{2}$ **c)** $\frac{1}{25}$ **e)** $\frac{33}{100}$ **g)** $\frac{1}{13}$

b) $\frac{1}{4}$ **d)** $\frac{2}{3}$ **f)** $\frac{9}{23}$ **h)** $\frac{2}{5}$

Q6 119 out of 140 houses on an estate have video recorders. What percentage is this?

Questions on Fractions without a Calculator

I know doing fractions by hand is pretty scary stuff — so you'd better learn those 4 Manual Methods.

1) Multiplying	*Multiply top and bottom separately:* $\frac{2}{5}\times\frac{3}{7}=\frac{2\times3}{5\times7}=\frac{6}{35}$
2) Dividing	*Turn the 2nd fraction UPSIDE DOWN and then multiply:* $\frac{2}{5}\div\frac{3}{7}=\frac{2}{5}\times\frac{7}{3}=\frac{2\times7}{5\times3}=\frac{14}{15}$
3) Adding, Subtracting	*Add or subtract TOP LINES ONLY, but only once the bottom numbers are the same:* $\frac{3}{5}+\frac{1}{5}=\frac{3+1}{5}$, $\frac{3}{5}-\frac{1}{5}=\frac{2}{5}$
4) Cancelling Down	*Divide top and bottom by the same number till they won't go any further:* $\frac{24}{32}=\frac{24\div8}{32\div8}=\frac{3}{4}$

Q1 Cancel these fractions to their lowest terms:

a) $\frac{7}{21}$ **c)** $\frac{3}{5}$ **e)** $\frac{25}{100}$

b) $\frac{30}{90}$ **d)** $\frac{7}{35}$ **f)** $\frac{11}{121}$

Once you've ploughed your way through this little lot, you'll find they're not all that bad.

Q2 Express these as improper fractions:

a) $1\frac{2}{3}$ **b)** $10\frac{1}{2}$ **c)** $3\frac{1}{4}$ **d)** $1\frac{8}{9}$ **e)** $2\frac{2}{5}$ **f)** $7\frac{3}{10}$

Q3 Arrange the following in ascending order:

$\frac{3}{6}$ $\frac{6}{3}$ $3\frac{1}{6}$ $6\frac{1}{3}$ $\frac{36}{3}$ $\frac{63}{6}$

Q4 Add the two fractions, giving your answer as a fraction in its lowest terms:

a) $\frac{7}{8}+\frac{3}{8}$ **b)** $\frac{1}{12}+\frac{3}{4}$ **c)** $1\frac{2}{5}+2\frac{2}{3}$ **d)** $\frac{1}{6}+4\frac{1}{3}$ **e)** $1\frac{3}{10}+\frac{2}{5}$

Q5 Evaluate, giving your answer as a fraction in its lowest terms:

a) $3\frac{1}{2}-\frac{2}{3}$ **b)** $10-\frac{2}{5}$ **c)** $1\frac{3}{4}-1\frac{1}{5}$ **d)** $4\frac{2}{3}-\frac{7}{9}$ **e)** $8-\frac{1}{8}$

Q6 Do the following multiplications, expressing the answers as fractions in their lowest terms:

a) $\frac{4}{3}\times\frac{3}{4}$ **b)** $2\frac{1}{6}\times3\frac{1}{3}$ **c)** $\frac{2}{5}\times\frac{3}{4}$ **d)** $2\frac{1}{2}\times\frac{3}{5}$ **e)** $10\frac{2}{7}\times\frac{7}{9}$

Q7 Carry out the following divisions, and express each answer in its lowest terms:

a) $\frac{1}{4}\div\frac{3}{8}$ **b)** $1\frac{1}{2}\div\frac{5}{12}$ **c)** $\frac{1}{9}\div\frac{2}{3}$ **d)** $10\frac{4}{5}\div\frac{9}{10}$

Q8 Simplify the following:

a) $\dfrac{\left(\frac{1}{7}\times\frac{7}{8}\right)}{\frac{1}{8}}$ **b)** $\dfrac{\left(3\frac{1}{12}\div\frac{1}{6}\right)}{\left(1\frac{1}{5}\times\frac{5}{12}\right)}$ **c)** $\dfrac{\left(2\frac{2}{3}\right)}{\left(4\frac{1}{2}\times\frac{4}{3}\right)}$

Questions on Fractions without a Calculator

The cunning bit with these long wordy questions is picking out the important bits and then translating them into numbers. It's not that easy at first, but you'll get better — I guess you've just gotta learn to ignore the waffly stuff.

Q9 In the fast food café, over all the shifts there are eighteen girls and twelve boys waiting at tables. In the kitchen there are six boys and nine girls. What fraction of the kitchen staff are girls, and what fraction of the employees are boys?

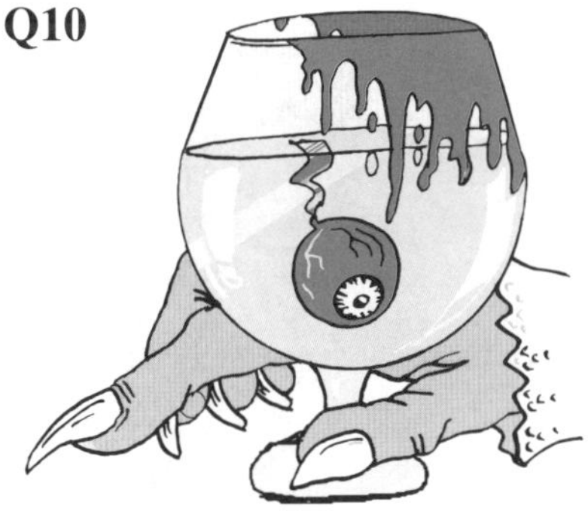

Q10 In a survey, people were asked if they liked a new cola drink. One in five thought it was great, four out of fifteen felt there was no difference in taste, three in ten disliked it and the rest offered no opinion.
What fraction of people offered no opinion?

Forget all about cola drinks and red trousers — just write it all as a sum, then do the calculation. Nowt to it.

Q11 Neil wore red trousers on a total of 12 days in November.

a) On what fraction of the total number of days in November did Neil wear red trousers?

b) For 1/5 of the days in November Neil wore a blue shirt. How many days is this?

Q12 What fraction of 1 hour is:

a) 5 minutes

b) 15 minutes

c) 40 minutes?

Q13 If a TV programme lasts 40 minutes, what fraction of the programme is left after:

a) 10 minutes

b) 15 minutes

c) 35 minutes?

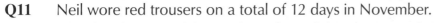

Q14 The Sandwich Club of Great Britain are going on their annual picnic.

a) If one sandwich is $\frac{5}{8}$ inches thick, how many layers of sandwiches can be stacked in a box 10 inches high?

b) How tall would the box need to be if 40 layers of sandwiches were to be stacked inside?

Questions on Fractions with a Calculator

Make sure you know the 5 things the fraction button `a b/c` does. It's really easy — you'd have to be crazy not to use it.

Q1 Say how to use the `a b/c` button to enter the following normal fractions.

a) $\frac{1}{3}$ just press `1` `a b/c` `3` b) $\frac{1}{4}$ c) $\frac{3}{4}$ d) $\frac{7}{90}$

Q2 Say how to use the `a b/c` button to enter the following mixed fractions.

a) $2\frac{1}{3}$ just press `2` `a b/c` `1` `a b/c` `3` b) $1\frac{1}{4}$ c) $3\frac{7}{9}$ d) $2\frac{1}{6}$

Q3 Use the `a b/c` button to calculate the following

a) $\frac{1}{3}+\frac{1}{4}$ c) $\frac{1}{7}\times\frac{14}{9}$ e) $9\frac{6}{7}\times\frac{14}{3}$

b) $\frac{1}{6}+\frac{4}{5}$ d) $1\frac{1}{3}-\frac{3}{4}$ f) $\frac{1}{3}\times\frac{3}{4}\times\frac{4}{6}$

Q4 Using the `a b/c` button and the `=` button reduce these fractions to their lowest terms:

a) $\frac{15}{30}$ b) $\frac{6}{9}$ c) $\frac{18}{24}$ d) $\frac{100}{250}$ e) $\frac{7}{49}$ f) $\frac{9}{108}$

Q5 Use the `SHIFT` button and the `a b/c` button to turn these mixed fractions into top heavy fractions. (You might need the `=` button as well.)

a) $2\frac{3}{4}$ c) $11\frac{6}{13}$ e) $8\frac{9}{11}$

b) $9\frac{3}{4}$ d) $12\frac{4}{9}$ f) $7\frac{3}{16}$

Don't panic if you haven't got a `SHIFT` button because you'll have a `2nd` or `INV` button instead — they do the same job. Hurrah.

Q6 The wage bill at an office is £2400 in total. Fred gets one sixth, Greg gets a fifth of the remainder and Hillary gets what is left. How much money are each of them paid?

Q7 If I pay my gas bill within seven days, I can have a reduction of an eighth of the price. If my bill is £120, how much can I save?

Q8 Jody sold her drum kit for £360 when she decided to buy a stereo. She lost a fifth of her money, but then needed to save only the remaining one tenth of the stereo's price. How much was the drum kit originally, and how much was the stereo?

Phew, thank goodness, that's the last page on fractions — but make sure you did all the questions — it's all on the Syllabus.

Questions on Percentages

Take it from me, there are three distinct types of percentage question — and one is easier than the other two. Basically, if you can see the % symbol you're onto a winner. Try these questions and you'll see what I mean.

1) "OF" means "×".
2) "PER CENT" means "OUT OF 100".

Example: 30% of 150 would be translated as $\frac{30}{100} \times 150 = 45$.

Q1 Calculate:

a) 50% of £25.00
b) 20% of £5.25
c) 5% of £3.60
d) 36% of 400 kg
e) 12% of 75 g
f) 7% of 50 g
g) 12% of 300 rabbits
h) 18% of 150 cars
i) 0.5% of 89 m.

Q2 Terry has earnt £56 by washing cars. Whilst shopping he spent <u>20%</u> of his earnings on a CD, <u>5%</u> on his lunch and paid the rest into the bank.

a) How much money did Terry spend on food?
b) How much money did the CD cost?

Q3 John bought a new PC. The tag in the shop said it cost <u>£890 + VAT</u>.

If VAT is charged at 17½%, how much did he pay?

Finding "something %" of "something else" is really quite simple — so you'd better be sure you know how.

Q4 The admission price at Wonder World is <u>£18 for adults</u>. A child's ticket costs <u>60%</u> of the adult price.

a) How much will it cost for one adult and 4 children to enter Wonder World?
b) How much will two adults and three children spend on entrance tickets?

Q5 A double glazing salesman is paid 10% commission on every sale he makes.
In addition he is paid a £50 bonus if the sale is over £500.

a) If a customer buys £499 worth of windows from the salesman, what is his <u>commission</u>?
b) How much extra will he earn if he can persuade the customer in part **a)** to spend an extra £20?
c) How much does he earn if he sells £820 worth of windows?

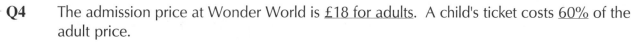

Q6 Daphne earns an annual wage of £18900. She doesn't pay tax on the first £3400 that she earns. How much income tax does she pay when the rate of tax is:

a) 25% ?
b) 40% ?

Questions on Percentages

Make mighty sure you can see the difference between the two types of question on this page — if you're struggling have a gander at P.26 and P.27 of The Revision Guide.

Look for the word "percentage" to spot the second type of percentage question. It's not as bad as it looks — well not once you know the method:

Fraction — Decimal — Percentage	Express 25p as a percentage of £1.25
1) Put the two numbers together as a fraction. 2) Divide them to make a decimal. 3) Multiply by 100 to make a percentage.	1) $\frac{25}{125}$ 2) 25 ÷ 125 = 0.2 3) 0.2 × 100 = 20%

Q7 A boat manufacturer reduces the price of its small rubber dinghy from £42.00 to £31.50. What is the percentage reduction?

Q8 At birth, a certain African elephant measured 1.2 m tall. When the elephant was fully grown she was 3.5 m tall. Calculate the percentage increase in height over her lifetime.

Q9 Rockwood School's results for A-Level biology are given in the table.

A-Level Biology Results

Grade	A	B	C	D	E
Frequency	7	10	15	12	5

a) What percentage of candidates achieved grade A?

b) What percentage of candidates achieved grades A, B or C?

c) What percentage of candidates didn't achieve grades A, B or C?

Q10 There are approximately 9000 burger bars in the UK. Every day about 320 people visit each one. Given that the population of the UK is roughly 60 million, approximately what percentage of the population visit a burger bar each day?

Most people get the third type wrong — but only because they don't recognise them and use the simple method:

Example: A house rose in value by 25% to £62,000 over the past year. What was its value a year ago?

Method: £62,000 = 125%
(÷125) £496 = 1%
(×100) £49,600 = 100%
So the value a year ago was £49,600.

An increase of 25% means that £62,000 represents 125% of the original value.
(If it had been a reduction, £62,000 would have represented 75% of the original value.)

Q11 An antiques expert estimates that his collection of fine Victorian table mats is increasing in value at a rate of 9% every year. Today the collection is worth £436.

a) How much was his collection worth a year ago?

b) How much will his collection be worth one year from now?

Questions on Growth and Decay

Hey look — it's another of those "<u>there is only one formula to learn and you use it for every question</u>" topics.

So I reckon you'd better learn <u>The Formula</u> then...

The Compound Growth and Decay Formula

$$N = N_0\left(1 + {}^{r}\!/_{100}\right)^n$$

- N — Amount after a number of hours/days/years
- N_0 — Initial amount
- r — Percentage change per hour/day/year
- n — Number of hours/days/years

Q1 Calculate the amount in each account if:

a) £200 is invested for 10 yrs at 9% compound interest per annum
b) £500 is invested for 3 yrs at 7% compound interest per annum
c) £750 is invested for 30 months at 8% compound interest per annum
d) £1000 is invested for 15 months at 6.5% compound interest per annum.

Q2 A colony of bacteria grows at the compound rate of 12% per hour. Initially there are 200 bacteria.

a) How many will there be after 3 hours?
b) How many will there be after 1 day?

Just make sure you get the <u>increase</u> and <u>decrease</u> the right way round... basically, just check your answer sounds like you'd expect — and if it doesn't, <u>do it again</u>.

Q3 A radioactive element was observed every day and the mass remaining was measured. Initially there was 9 kg but this decreased at the compound rate of 3% per day. How much radioactive element will be left after:

a) 3 days
b) 6 days
c) 1 week
d) 4 weeks?

Give your answer to no more than 3 d.p.

Q4 Money is invested on the stock market. During a recession the value of the shares fall by 2% per week.
Find the value of the stock if:

a) £2000 was invested for a fortnight
b) £30,000 was invested for a month
c) £500 was invested for 7 weeks
d) £100,000 was invested for a year.

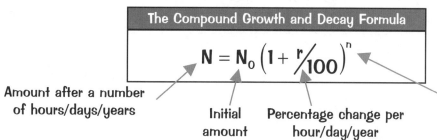

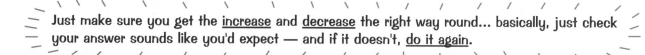

I'd go for Victorian rolling pins, myself...

Questions on Ratios

I don't want to spoil the surprise, but you're going to need your calculator for this bit — get your finger on that fraction button...

RATIOS are like FRACTIONS which are like DECIMALS

We can treat the RATIO 3:4 like the FRACTION $\frac{3}{4}$ which is 0.75 as a DECIMAL.

Watch out though — this isn't $\frac{3}{4}$ of the total: *If there are girls and boys in the ratio 3:4, it means there's $\frac{3}{4}$ as many girls as boys. So if there's 8 boys, there's $\frac{3}{4} \times 8 = 6$ girls.*

Q1 Write these ratios in their simplest forms:

a) 6:8 **b)** 5:20 **c)** 1.5:3 **d)** $2\frac{1}{4}$: 4 **e)** 2 weeks: 4 days **f)** £1.26:14p

Q2 Divide the following amounts in the ratio given:

a) £20 in the ratio 2:3 **b)** 500 g in the ratio 1:2:2 **c)** 150 m in the ratio 8:7

Q3 John and Peter share a bar of chocolate marked into 16 squares. They share it in the ratio 1:3. How many squares does each boy get?

Q4 A recipe for flapjacks uses 250 g of oats, 150 g of brown sugar and 100 g of margarine. What fraction of the mixture is:

a) oats?

b) sugar?

Don't forget to check your units. (I reckon if I say it enough times, you'll eventually cave in and start doing it — betcha)

Q5

I picked some strawberries after a few wet days. Some were eaten by slugs, some were mouldy and some fine. The ratio was 2:3:10 respectively. If 9 strawberries were mouldy,

a) How many were good?

b) How many did I lose altogether?

c) What fraction of the total amount were good?

Q6 The plan of a house is drawn to a scale of 1 cm to 3 m.

a) Write this ratio in its simplest form.

b) How wide is a room that shows as 2 cm on the drawing?

c) How long will a 10 m hall look on the drawing?

Q7 The ratio of girls to boys in a school is 7:6. If there are 455 pupils in total, how many are

a) girls? **b)** boys?

Remember — for most questions the trick is to divide the total amount by the total number of parts (the ratio numbers added together). Then you multiply by each ratio number separately to find the different amounts.

Questions on Conversion Factors

The method for these questions is very easy so you might as well learn it...

> *1) Find the Conversion Factor (always easy)*
>
> *2) Multiply by it AND divide by it*
>
> *3) Choose the common sense answer*

Q1 Cashbags Bank are offering an exchange rate of 1.62 Euros for £1 Sterling. They are also offering 1.55 US Dollars for £1 Sterling and 185.5 Japanese Yen for £1 Sterling. Calculate, to the nearest penny, the Sterling equivalent of:

a) 200 Euros
b) 1121Yen
c) 5 Yen
d) 1.7 Euros
e) 345 Dollars
f) 1 Euro
g) 1 Dollar
h) 33.57 Dollars

Remember — multiply and divide then choose your answer.

Using the same exchange rates, convert the following amounts into Japanese Yen:

i) £100
j) 1 Dollar
k) 0.6 Euros
l) 255 Euros
m) £0.50
n) 120,000 Dollars

Q2 If 1 pint = 0.568 litres which is better value –
a) 2 pints of orange juice for \$0.72
or
b) 1 litre of orange juice for 49p?

Q3 The scale on a map is 1:15,000. How big are the following in real life:
a) a distance of 2 cm on the map
b) a distance of 20 cm on the map
c) a distance of 70 cm on the map
d) an area of 2 cm^2 on the map?

Maps are tricky, 'cos you've got to think about units. It's best to do the conversion in the units you're given, then do a second conversion to appropriate units.

Q4 Another map has a scale of 1:5,000. What size on this map are the following:
a) a distance of 5 km in real life
b) a distance of 1 km in real life
c) an area of 100 m^2 in real life
d) an area of 50 m^2 in real life?

Just remember — the distance on the map is unlikely to be larger than the real life distance.

Q5 A map is drawn on a scale of 5 cm = 25 km. A section of river is 15 km long. How many cm will this be on the map?

If you're struggling, take a look at P.31 of the revision guide to see how it's done.

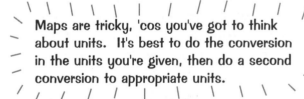

Questions on Standard Index Form

Writing very big (or very small) numbers gets a bit messy with all those zeros, if you don't use this standard index form. But of course, the main reason for knowing about standard form is...you guessed it — it's in the Exam.

Any numbers written in Standard Index Form always look like:

$a \times 10^n$

This number (a) must be between 1 and 10 but never equal to 10

This number (n) is equal to the number of places the decimal point moves.
n is +ve for larger numbers
n is -ve for small numbers

eg.

580000000000000000 = 5.8×10^{17}
43000000000000000000 = 4.3×10^{19}
0.0000000000000017 = 1.7×10^{-15}
0.00000000000000008 = 8×10^{-17}

Q1 Complete these two tables:

Number	Standard form
4500000000	
19300000000000	
	8.2×10^{12}
82000000	
	6.34×10^{8}
	4.02×10^{6}
423400000000	
	8.431×10^{7}
	1.03×10^{5}
4700	

Number	Standard form
0.000000006	
0.00000000072	
	8.5×10^{-6}
0.000000143	
	7.12×10^{-5}
	3.68×10^{-10}
	4.003×10^{-8}
0.0000009321	
	5.2×10^{-3}
	9.999×10^{-7}
0.00000000802	
	2.3104×10^{-6}
0.000001	

Q2 Rewrite the following, either in standard form or changing standard form to normal numbers.

a) Mercury is 694000000 km from the Sun.
b) The Sahara desert covers 8600000 km^2.
c) The Earth is approximately 4.5×10^9 years old.
d) The average depth of the Atlantic is 3.7×10^3 metres.
e) The charge on an electron is 1.6×10^{-19} Coulombs.
f) A Uranium nucleus can release 3.20×10^{-11} Joules of energy.
g) In Chemistry, Avogadro's constant is 6.033×10^{23}.
h) The circumference of the equator is 40076 km.
i) The population of the USA is approximately 249231000 people.
j) From Washington to Tokyo is 6763 miles.
k) A tonne of coal can produce 2.8×10^{10} Joules of energy.
l) The radius of the nucleus of an atom is 0.0000000000003 cm.
m) In 2050 the population of the world will be around 1.1×10^{10} people.

You may have noticed standard form is used a lot in science, so if you're a budding nuclear physicist, get learning. Oh, you're not. Well, you've still got to learn it. Sorry.

Q3 Find the value of the following, giving your answers in standard form.

a) $46 \times 4.2 \times 5000$
b) $20 \times 40 \times 50 \times 8.2$
c) $0.2 \times 0.3 \times 0.5 \times 0.1$
d) $5000 \div 0.02$
e) $62000 \div 0.31$
f) $40000000 \div 1000$

Questions on Standard Index Form

This stuff gets a lot easier if you know how to handle your calculator — read and learn.

Standard Index Form with a Calculator

Use the EXP button (or EE button) to enter numbers in standard index form.

Eg $1.7 \times 10^9 + 2.6 \times 10^{10}$ 1 . 7 EXP 9 + 2 . 6 EXP 10 =

The answer is 2.77 10 which is read as 2.77×10^{10}

Q4 If $x = 4 \times 10^5$ and $y = 6 \times 10^4$ work out the value of
a) xy **b)** 4x **c)** 3y.

Q5 Which is greater, 4.62×10^{12} or 1.04×10^{13}, and by how much?

Q6 Which is smaller, 3.2×10^{-8} or 1.3×10^{-9}, and by how much?

Q7 The following numbers are not written in standard index form. Rewrite them correctly using standard index form.

a) 42×10^6
b) 38×10^{-5}
c) 10×10^6
d) 11.2×10^{-5}
e) 843×10^3
f) 42.32×10^{-4}
g) 17×10^{17}
h) 28.3×10^{-5}
i) 10×10^{-3}

Don't forget — when you're using a calculator, you've got to write the answer as 3.46 × 10^27, not as 3.46^27. If you do it the wrong way, it means something completely different.

Q8 What is 7 million in standard index form?

Q9 The radius of the Earth is 6.38×10^3 km. What is the radius of the Earth measured in cm? Leave your answer in standard form.

Q10 a) The surface area of the Earth is approximately 5.1×10^8 km². Write this without using standard form.
b) The area of the Earth covered by sea is 362 000 000 km². Write this in standard form.
c) What is the approximate area of the Earth covered by land? Write your answer without using standard form.

Q11 The length of a light year, the distance light can travel in one year, is 9.461×10^{15} m. How far can light travel in
a) 2 years?
b) 6 months?
Write your answers in standard form.

Q12 One atomic mass unit is equivalent to 1.661×10^{-27} kg. What are two atomic mass units equivalent to (in standard index form)?

Questions on Rounding Off

There are two ways of choosing where to round a number off — Decimal Places is the easiest.

The Basic Method Has Three Steps

1) Identify the position of the LAST DIGIT.
2) Then look at the next digit to the RIGHT — called the DECIDER.
3) If the DECIDER is 5 or more, then ROUND UP the LAST DIGIT.
   If the DECIDER is less than 5, then leave the LAST DIGIT as it is.

Q1 David divides £15.20 by 3. What is the answer to the nearest penny?

Q2 A bumper bag of icing sugar weighs 23.4 kg. What is this correct to the nearest kilogram?

Q3 Round these numbers to the required number of decimal places:

a) 62.1935 (1 dp)
b) 62.1935 (2 dp)
c) 62.1935 (3 dp)
d) 19.624328 (5 dp)
e) 6.2999 (3 dp)
f) π (3 dp)

'dp' means the number of digits to the right of the decimal point.

SIGNIFICANT FIGURES

1) The 1st significant figure of any number is simply THE FIRST DIGIT WHICH ISN'T ZERO.
2) The 2nd, 3rd, 4th, etc. significant figures follow immediately after the 1st, REGARDLESS OF BEING ZEROS OR NOT ZEROS.
3) After Rounding Off the LAST DIGIT, end ZEROS must be filled in up to, BUT NOT BEYOND, the decimal point.

Q4 Round these numbers to the required number of significant figures:

a) 1329.62 (3 SF)
b) 1329.62 (4 SF)
c) 1329.62 (5 SF)
d) 120 (1 SF)
e) 0.024687 (1 SF)
f) 0.024687 (4 SF)

Q5 At a golf club, a putting green is given as being 5 m long to the nearest metre. Give the range of values that the actual length of the green could be.

Q6

Carlo weighs himself on some scales that are accurate to the nearest 10 g. The digital display shows his weight as 142.46 kg.

a) What is the maximum that he could weigh?
b) What is the minimum that he could weigh?

Q7 Claudia ran a 100 m race in 11.6 seconds. If the time was measured to the nearest 0.1 seconds and the distance to the nearest metre, what is the maximum value of her average speed, in metres per second?

Questions on Accuracy and Estimating

We're still on Significant Figures — I hope you enjoyed the last page. Still, it's all good practice, and practice makes...

1) For fairly CASUAL MEASUREMENTS, 2 SIGNIFICANT FIGURES are most appropriate.

Cooking – 250 g (2 sig fig) of sugar, not 253 g (3 SF) or 300 g (1 SF)

2) For IMPORTANT OR TECHNICAL THINGS, 3 SIGNIFICANT FIGURES are essential.

A length that will be cut to fit, eg you'd measure a shelf as 25.6 cm long, not 26 cm or 25.63 cm.

3) Only for REALLY SCIENTIFIC WORK would you need over 3 SIGNIFICANT FIGURES.

Only someone really keen would want to know the length of a piece of string to the nearest tenth of a millimetre – like 34.46 cm, for example.

Q1 Decide on an appropriate degree of accuracy for the following:

a) the total dry weight, 80872 kg, of the space shuttle OV-102 Columbia with its 3 main engines
b) the distance of 3.872 miles from Mel's house to Bryan's house
c) 1.563 m of fabric required to make a bedroom curtain
d) 152.016 kg of coal delivered to Jeff's house
e) 6 buses owned by the Partridge Flight Bus Company
f) the maximum night temperature of 11.721°C forecast for Birmingham by a TV weather presenter.

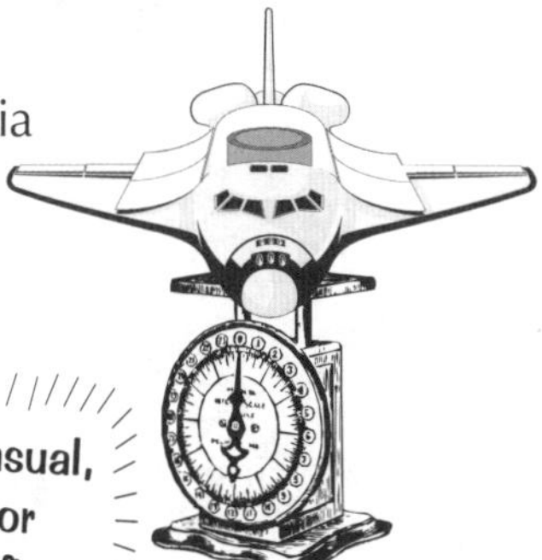

Just think casual, technical or really scientific...

ESTIMATING the ANSWER to a CALCULATION

1) ROUND EVERYTHING OFF to nice easy CONVENIENT NUMBERS
2) Then WORK OUT THE ANSWER using those nice easy numbers.

Q2 Estimate the square roots of these numbers **without** using a calculator:

a) 67 **b)** 22 **c)** 117 **d)** 50 **e)** 10

Always show your workings — you'll lose easy marks if you don't — so I guess it's worth doing.

ESTIMATING AREAS and VOLUMES

1) Draw or imagine a RECTANGLE OR CUBOID of similar size to the object in question.
2) ROUND OFF ALL LENGTHS to the NEAREST WHOLE, and work it out.

Q3 Estimate the following:

a) Estimate the Area of the island

b) Estimate the Volume of the glass

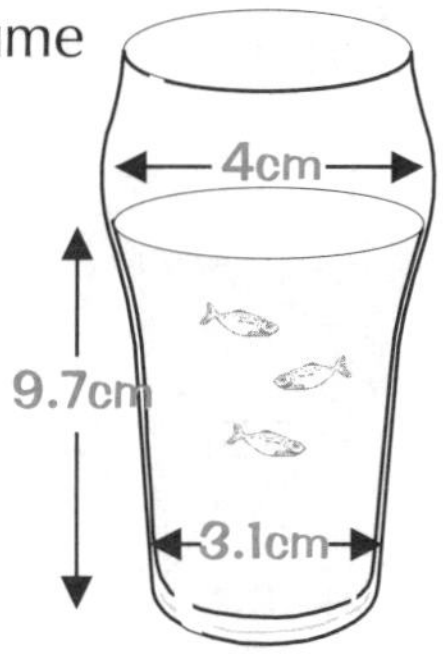

Questions on Calculator Buttons

Calculators can work wonders, and it's a good idea to find out what those wonders are. You'll save yourself loads of time in the Exam — and that means you can spend more time on the really hard stuff. Hmmm...

The SQUARE, SQUARE ROOT and CUBE ROOT buttons are [x^2] [$\sqrt{\ }$] [$\sqrt[3]{\ }$]

1) The [x^2] button squares the number in the display, ie IT MULTIPLIES IT BY ITSELF.
2) [$\sqrt{\ }$] is the REVERSE PROCESS of [x^2] — it gives the SQUARE ROOT.
3) [$\sqrt[3]{\ }$] gives the CUBE ROOT of the number in the display. This is sometimes a 2nd function button.

Q1 Using the [x^2] button on your calculator, work out:

a) 1^2 **d)** 15^2 **g)** $(-4)^2$
b) 12^2 **e)** $(-3)^2$ **h)** 1000^2
c) 2^2 **f)** 20^2 **i)** 0^2

(For parts **e)** and **g)** use the button marked [+/-] or [(-)].)

OK, you probably know some of the answers already, but at least it checks your calculator actually works.

Q2 Using the [$\sqrt{\ }$] button on your calculator work out:

a) $\sqrt{25}$ **d)** $\sqrt{5}$ **g)** $\sqrt{2500}$
b) $\sqrt{0}$ **e)** $\sqrt{20}$ **h)** $\sqrt{900}$
c) $\sqrt{169}$ **f)** $\sqrt{36}$ **i)** $\sqrt{2}$

Q3 Use the [$\sqrt[3]{\ }$] button on your calculator to work out:

a) $\sqrt[3]{1}$ **c)** $\sqrt[3]{0}$ **e)** $\sqrt[3]{8}$ **g)** $\sqrt[3]{27}$
b) $\sqrt[3]{64}$ **d)** $\sqrt[3]{1000000}$ **f)** $\sqrt[3]{-27}$ **h)** $\sqrt[3]{3}$

Q4 For his birthday Lars Larson was given a new calculator. He pressed the button [2], then he pressed [x^2] 12 times, and finally he pressed [=]. Much to Lars' alarm, a funny message appeared in the display. What did it mean?

The MEMORY BUTTONS are usually labelled [STO] (store) and [RCL] (recall).

On some calculators the memory buttons are [Min] (Memory In) and [MR] (Memory Recall).

Q5 By calculating the bottom line first (the denominator) then using your calculator's memory buttons, work out

a) $\dfrac{19}{1+\sin(45°)}$ **c)** $\dfrac{20}{\cos(45°)+9}$ **e)** $\dfrac{16}{12+\tan(45°)}$

b) $\dfrac{\tan(12°)}{16+18^2}$ **d)** $\dfrac{71}{6+\sqrt[3]{9}}$ **f)** $\dfrac{10}{17\times\tan(6°)}$

Yeah, you could write the answer down at each step, but don't. Let your calculator do the work — that's what it's there for.

Questions on Calculator Buttons

OK, so some of these buttons look pretty confusing, but it's really important that you get to grips with exactly what they do:

Calculators work things out in a certain order:
Brackets, Other, Division, Multiplication, Addition, Subtraction.

eg $\frac{12+13}{46-17}$. Pressing 12 + 13 ÷ 46 – 17 = will give you completely the wrong answer. The calculator will think you mean 12 + 13/46 – 17, because the calculator will do the division before the addition and subtraction. Use the brackets buttons to override BODMAS:

[(--- 12 + 13 ---)] ÷ [(--- 46 – 17 ---)] =

Q6 Using [(--- and ---)] in an appropriate manner, calculate:

a) $\frac{(23+9)}{(4\times4)}$ **b)** $\frac{6}{(1\times3)(7-5)}$ **c)** $\frac{(8+(6\div2))}{(8\times2)}$ **d)** $\frac{1\times2}{3\times4}$ **e)** $\frac{6}{(6+2)(4-2)}$ **f)** $\frac{4(4+2)}{6(1\times4)}$

Brackets always come in pairs — one bracket on its own is about as much use as one shoe. It's as simple as that.

Q7 Using the X^y button on your calculator, find:

a) 1^0 **b)** 3^{10} **c)** 2^{20} **d)** π^3 **e)** 4^{10} **f)** $(\tan45°)^{10}$ **g)** 8^5 **h)** $(\sin30°)^2$

For entering numbers into your calculator in standard form you need the EXP or EE button. It actually means <u>x 10</u>^{n} so be careful not to type in the <u>x 10</u> part.

E.g. to enter 3.4 x 10^5 you would only need to type 3 • 4 EXP 5 =

and <u>not</u> 3 • 4 × 10 X^y 5 =

Q8 Enter the following numbers into your calculator and write down what you get:

a) 4×10^3 **b)** 1×10^4 **c)** 6.2×10^5

Q9 Work out (leaving your answers in standard form):

a) $\frac{2\times10^2}{5\times10^1}$ **b)** $\frac{4.2\times10^4}{2.1\times10^5}$ **c)** $\frac{1.92\times10^3}{9.6\times10^2}$ **d)** $\frac{2.3\times10^5}{4.6\times10^6}$ **e)** $\frac{7.0\times10^3}{3.5\times10^5}$ **f)** $\frac{4.44\times10^4}{1.11\times10^2}$

Make sure you know where your standard form button is. Take it from me, you'll definitely need it in the Exam.

Questions on Special Number Sequences

There are five special sequences: EVEN, ODD, SQUARE, CUBE and TRIANGLE NUMBERS. You really need to know them and their n^{th} terms.

Q1 What are these sequences called, and what are their next 3 terms?

a) 2, 4, 6, 8, ...
b) 1, 3, 5, 7, ...
c) 1, 4, 9, 16, ...
d) 1, 8, 27, 64, ...
e) 1, 3, 6, 10, ...

Q2 The following sequences are described in words. Write down their first four terms.

a) The prime numbers starting from 37.
b) The powers of 2 starting from 32.
c) The squares of odd numbers starting from $7^2 = 49$.
d) The triangular numbers starting from 15.
e) The powers of 10 starting from 1000.

Q3 Find the nth term of the following sequences:

a) 2, 4, 6, 8, ...
b) 1, 3, 5, 7, ...
c) 1, 4, 9, 16, ...
d) 4, 8, 16, 32, ...
e) 1, 8, 27, 64, ...
f) 1, 3, 6, 10, ...

Q4

Sequence A	*1, 4, 9, 16, 25,...*
Sequence B	*3, 6, 9, 12, 15,...*
Sequence C	*2, 5, 9, 14, 20,...*

You should recognise sequences A and B, but I'm not sure I recognise sequence C.

a) Write down the next three terms in sequence A.
b) Write down the next three terms in sequence B.
c) Write down the nth term of sequence A.
d) Write down the nth term of sequence B.
e) Sequence C is obtained from sequences A and B. Using this information and your answers to parts **c)** and **d)** work out the nth term for sequence C.
f) Calculate the 80th term of sequence C.

Q5 The first four terms of a sequence are x, 4x, 9x, 16x.

a) For x = 2 write down the next two terms in the sequence.
b) For x = 2 write down the nth term in the sequence.
c) For x = 3 write down the nth term in the sequence.
d) Write down the nth term, valid for any value of x.
e) For x = ½ calculate the 75th term in the sequence.

Questions on Number Patterns

In the Exam you'll probably have to find the nth term of a sequence. To get full marks you need to know how to handle the "Common Difference Type" and the "Changing Difference Type". Have a look at P.44 of the revision guide if you need a hand.

Q1 Using matchsticks, Jessica made a simple diagram of a house: If houses that are joined together still require their own roof,

a) how many matchsticks would she need to complete a pair of semi-detached houses?

b) how many matchsticks would she need to complete a set of three terraced houses?

c) how many matchsticks would she need to make four terraced houses?

d) what is the formula for a terrace of n houses?

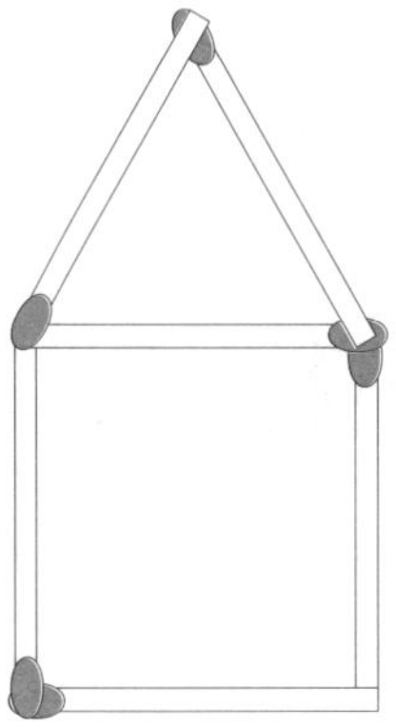

This is what you need to know to find the nth term of a "Common Difference Type" sequence:

Common Difference Type: nth term = dn + (a–d)

1) "a" is the FIRST TERM in the sequence.
2) "d" is the COMMON DIFFERENCE.

Q2 In the following sequences, write down the next 3 terms and the nth term:

a) 2, 5, 8, 11,...

b) 7, 12, 17, 22,...

c) 1, 11, 21, 31,...

d) 49, 56, 63, 70,...

Q3 Jeff is collecting the post for his grandmother while she is away on holiday. On the first day she was away she received 3 letters. On the second day the pile of letters had grown to 6. By the third day, Jeff had 9 letters in all. This pattern continued while his grandmother was away, and she returned from her holiday on the ninth day.

a) How many letters were waiting for her?

b) How many letters would have been waiting if she had returned on the nth day?

Changing Difference Type: nth term = a + (n-1)d + ½(n-1)(n-2)C

1) "a" is the first term in the sequence,
2) "d" is the first difference and
3) "C" is the change between one difference and the next.

Q4 Write down the next three terms and nth term of:

a) 2, 5, 9, 14,...

b) 3, 6, 11, 18,...

c) 6, 9, 16, 27,...

d) 11, 16, 24, 35,...

Another type, another formula. Use this for "Changing Difference" Sequences. It looks like a nightmare, I admit, but all you have to do is pop in the values of a, d and C and you're away.

Questions on Number Patterns

There are six main types of number sequence, but you'll only be asked to find the nth term for two. That means only two formulas, can't say fairer than that.

Q5 The nth term of a sequence is n(n + 1).

a) Write down the first 3 terms (n = 1,2,3...).

b) Explain why every term in the sequence is even.

c) Write down the nth term of another sequence in which every term is even.

d) Write down the nth term of a sequence in which every term is odd.

COMMON MULTIPLIER	COMMON DIVIDER
This type of number pattern has a <u>common multiplier</u> linking each pair of numbers. eg 5, 10, 20, 40,... *In this case the <u>common multiplier</u> is 2.*	*This type has a <u>common divider</u> linking each pair of numbers.* eg 189, 63, 21, 7,... *In this case the <u>common divider</u> is 3.*

Q6 For each of the following sequences, write down the next three terms:

a) 1, 4, 16, 64,...

b) 3, 15, 75, 375,...

c) 6, 12, 24, 48,...

d) 9, 27, 81, 243,...

Q7 Bryan collects stamps. In order to increase his collection he placed an advert in a national newspaper asking members of the public to send him stamps. On the 1st day he received 2 stamps. On the 2nd day he had received 6 stamps in total. By the end of the third day he had received 18 stamps in total. Assuming the same pattern continues, how many stamps had Bryan received by the end of the:

a) 4th day

b) 6th day

c) 10th day

d) nth day.

Q8 For each of the following sequences, write down the next three terms:

a) 729, 243, 81, 27,...

b) 31250, 6250, 1250, 250,...

c) 12288, 3072, 768, 192,...

d) 5103, 1701, 567, 189,...

Q9 In order to work out the evaporation rate, Joanna measured the area of a puddle of water every hour on the hour. At 13:00 the area of the puddle was 128 cm^2. 1 hour later the area of the puddle was 64 cm^2. At 15:00 the area was 32 cm^2. Assuming the same pattern continues,

a) what was the area of the puddle of water at 16:00?

b) what was the area of the puddle at 18:00?

Questions on Basic Algebra

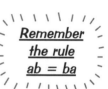

OK, it says basic, but it isn't a doddle. Things'll easily go wrong unless you really think about what you're doing — keep going 'til your brain hurts.

***Simplifying** means collecting **like terms** together:*	***Expanding** means removing brackets:*
$8x^2 + 2x + 4x^2 - x + 4$ becomes $12x^2 + x + 4$ (x^2 term, x term, x^2 term, x term, number term)	Eg $4(x + y) = 4x + 4y$ $x(2 + x) = 2x + x^2$ $-(a + b) = -a - b$

Q1 By collecting like terms, simplify the following:

a) $3x + 4y + 12x - 5y$
b) $11a + 6b + 24a + 18b$
c) $9f + 16g - 15f - 30g$
d) $14ab + 12cd - ab + 2cd$
e) $4x^2 + 3x + 2x^2 - 5x$
f) $13x^2 - 9x - x^2 + 4x$
g) $3y^2 + 2y - 4 + 8y^2 - y + 10$
h) $5xy + 6x + 2xy + 12x$
i) $9abc + 10ab + 14abc$
j) $13xy + 7yx$

Remember the rule ab = ba

Q2 Simplify the following:

a) $x \times x$
b) $2x \times x$
c) $2x \times 2x$
d) $3a \times 4b$
e) $6p \times 2q$
f) $8f \times 3g$
g) $2d \times {}^-4e$
h) $2 \times a \times b$
i) $3 \times x \times y$
j) $4 \times x \times x \times 0$
k) $20x \div 4$
l) $4x \div y$
m) $x^3 \div x^2$
n) $12ab \div 3$
o) $40y^2 \div 8y$

Q3 Remove the brackets and simplify if possible:

a) $2(x + y)$
b) $4(x - y)$
c) $8(x^2 + y^2)$
d) $12(x - 2)$
e) $-2(x - 5)$
f) $-(y - 2)$
g) $x(y + 2)$
h) $x(y + x)$
i) $x(x + y + z)$
j) $8(a + b) + 2(a + b)$
k) $3(x + y) + 4(x + 3y)$
l) $9(x + y) - 2(x + y)$
m) $4(a + 2b) - (a + 2b)$
n) $4(x - 2) - 2(x - 1)$
o) $14(2m - n) + 2(3n - 6m)$

Q4 Simplify the following:

a) $x(x + 1)$
b) $-2(4 + x)$
c) $-(z + 1)$
d) $x^2(2 + y)$
e) $x^2(3x + 4 + y)$
f) $5(p^3 + p)$
g) $15(2q + 3r^2)$
h) $-4(e^2 - f + 4)$
i) $2p(p + q) - 3p(p + 2q)$
j) $2x(4 + x) + 3x(x - 1)$
k) $x(2x + y) + 3y(3x + 2y)$
l) $a(b + c) + b(a + c) + c(a + b)$

Cancel algebraic fractions by looking for common factors on both the top and bottom lines, and cancelling them.	Eg $\dfrac{4xyz(x-2)(x-3)}{8x(x-2)} = \dfrac{yz(x-3)}{2}$

Q5 Simplify the following algebraic fractions by cancelling any common factors.

a) $\dfrac{xyz}{xy}$

b) $\dfrac{a(b-4)}{(b-4)}$

c) $\dfrac{4xy(z-3)(z+2)}{2x(z+2)}$

d) $\dfrac{9x^2y^2z(x-2)}{3xyz(x-2)}$

e) $\dfrac{3(a-4)^2(a-2)(a-1)}{9bc(a-1)(a-4)}$

f) $\dfrac{12x^2(a-4)^3(y-9)^4}{3x(a-4)^2(y-9)^2(z-2)}$

Questions on Basic Algebra

It's best to stick to this method — otherwise you're bound to miss one of the terms.

To multiply out double brackets use <u>FOIL</u>:

<u>F</u>irst	— Multiply the first terms in each bracket	Eg $(x + 2)(3x - 4)$
<u>O</u>utside	— Multiply the outside terms	$= (x \times 3x) + (x \times -4) + (2 \times 3x) + (2 \times -4)$
<u>I</u>nside	— Multiply the inside terms	$= 3x^2 - 4x + 6x - 8$
<u>L</u>ast	— Multiply the last terms	$= 3x^2 + 2x - 8$

Q6 For each of the large rectangles below, write down the <u>area</u> of the four smaller rectangles.

a)

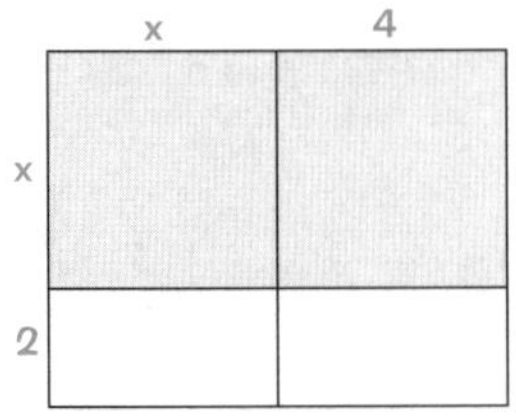

b)

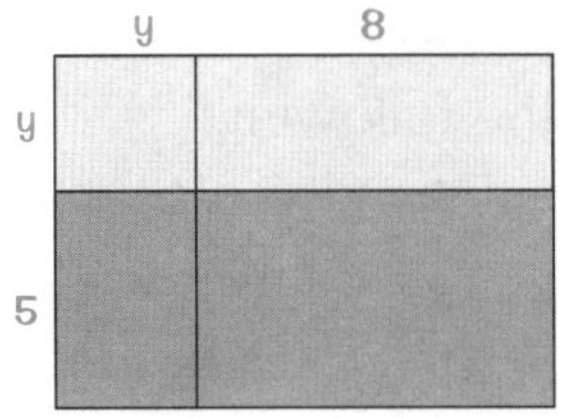

c)

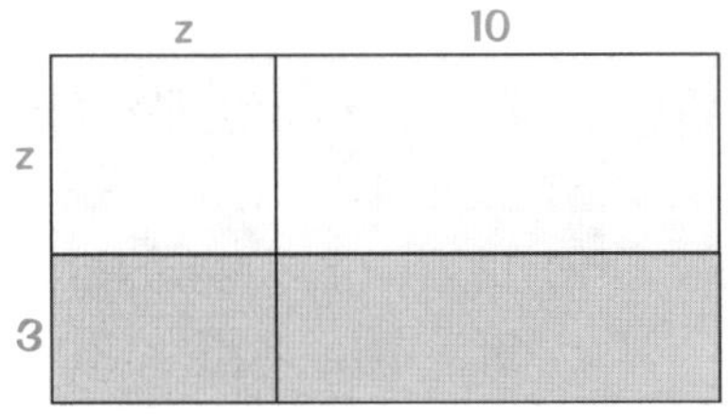

Q7 Multiply out the brackets and simplify your answers where possible:

a) $(x + 4)(x + 2)$
b) $(y + 8)(y + 5)$
c) $(z + 10)(z + 3)$
(Use your answers to **Q6** to help you check you've multiplied out the brackets correctly.)

Q8 Remove the brackets and simplify:

a) $(x + 1)(x + 2)$
b) $(x + 3)(x + 2)$
c) $(x + 4)(x + 5)$
d) $(x + 10)(x + 2)$
e) $(x + 5)(x - 1)$
f) $(x + 2)(x - 3)$
g) $(x - 3)(x + 1)$
h) $(x - 4)(x + 5)$
i) $(x - 2)(x - 1)$
j) $(x - 3)(x - 4)$
k) $(x - 2)(x - 5)$
l) $(x - 10)(x - 3)$
m) $(x - 5)(x + 10)$
n) $(5 + x)(2 + x)$
o) $(x - 2)(3 + x)$
p) $(4 - x)(8 - x)$

Q9 For each large rectangle write down the area of the four <u>small</u> rectangles, and hence find an <u>expression</u> for the area of the <u>large</u> rectangle.

a)

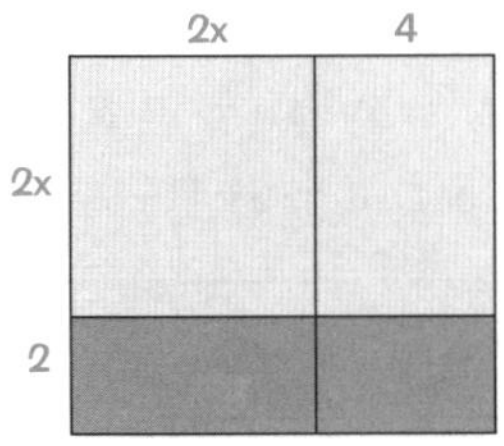

b)

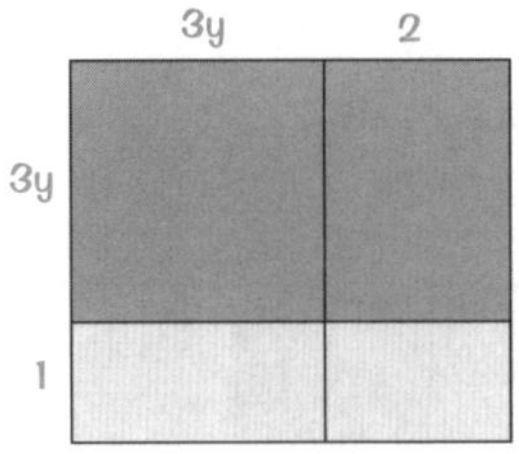

c)

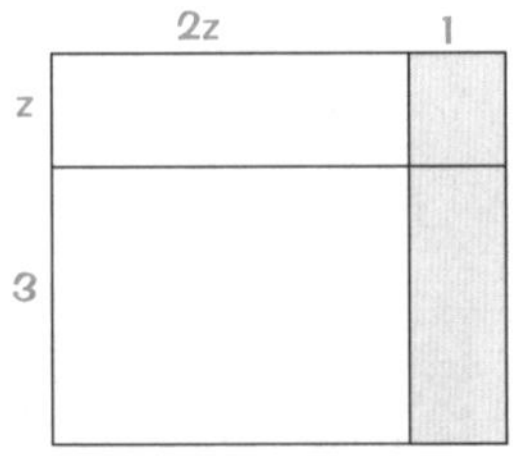

Q10 By removing the brackets, simplify the following:

a) $(2x + 1)(2x + 2)$
b) $(2x + 3)(x + 1)$
c) $(3x + 2)(3x + 4)$
d) $(3x + 1)(x + 2)$
e) $(2x - 1)(2x - 2)$
f) $(2x - 3)(2x - 2)$
g) $(3x - 1)(3x - 1)$
h) $(4x - 2)(4x - 3)$
i) $(2 + 2x)(2x - 1)$
j) $(3 + 2x)(x - 2)$
k) $(4 + 2x)(x - 1)$
l) $(x - 3)(2x + 1)$
m) $(2x - 5)(x + 10)$
n) $(x - 1)(7x + 12)$
o) $(6x + 2)(1 - x)$
p) $(3x + 2)(2x + 3)$

Questions on Basic Algebra

***FACTORISING** is just putting the brackets back in.*
And when you've just spent all that time getting rid of them...

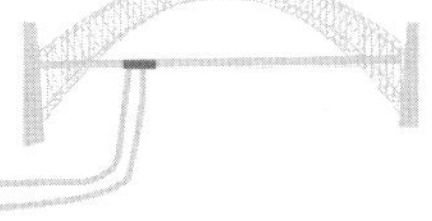

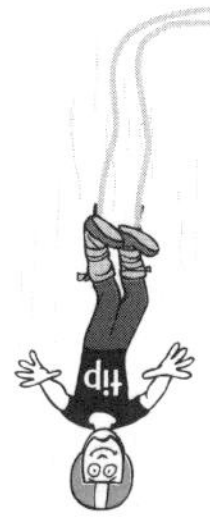

$$7x^2 + 21xy = 7x(x + 3y)$$

- largest number that will go into 7 and 21
- highest power of x, that will go into each term
- y is not in every term so it is not a common factor, and goes inside the brackets

Q11 Rewrite these expressions using brackets. Look for any common factors.

a) $2x + 4y$ **b)** $3x + 12y$ **c)** $9x + 3y$ **d)** $16x + 4y$
e) $2x + 12$ **f)** $3x + 15$ **g)** $24 + 12x$ **h)** $30 + 10x$
i) $4x - 40$ **j)** $5x - 15$ **k)** $7x - 49$ **l)** $8x - 32$
m) $10x - 8y$ **n)** $36x - 27y$ **o)** $24x - 32y$ **p)** $24x - 42$

Q12 Each expression below has 2x as a common factor. Factorise the following:

a) $2xy + 4x^2$ **b)** $2xy - 8x^2$
c) $2xy - 16x^2z$ **d)** $4xy - 6x^2$
e) $10x^2 - 6x^2$ **f)** $10x^2 - 6x$
g) $2xy - 4xz$ **h)** $12xy + 10xz$

Q13 Factorise:

a) $2yx + yz + 3yz$ **b)** $4ab + 2ac - ad$ **c)** $9pq + 6pr + 3ps$

Q14 Each term below has a^2 as a common factor. Factorise the following:

a) $a^2b + a^2c$ **b)** $4a^2 + 7a^2$ **c)** $5a^2 + 13a^2b$
d) $2a^2b + 3a^2c$ **e)** $10a^2b^2 + 9a^2c^2$ **f)** $a^3 + a^2y$
g) $2a^2x + 3a^2y + 4a^2z$ **h)** $2a^2b + 3a^2c + a^2$ **i)** $a^2b^2 + a^2c^2$

Q15 Each term below has x^2y as a common factor. Factorise the following:

a) $2x^2y + 3x^2y$ **b)** $9x^2y + 8x^2y$
c) $11x^2y + x^2y^2$ **d)** $5x^2y + 4x^2y^2$
e) $x^2y + x^2y^2$ **f)** $x^2y + x^3y + x^2y^2$

Q16 Each term below has 4xyz as a common factor. Factorise the following:

a) $4xyz + 8xyz$ **b)** $8xyz + 12xyz$
c) $8xyz + 16x^2yz$ **d)** $20x^2y^2z + 16xyz^2$

Q17 Factorise each of the following:

a) $2x + 6$ **b)** $4x + 16$ **c)** $5x + 30$ **d)** $3x - 18$ **e)** $2x + xy$
f) $3y + xy$ **g)** $3y + xy^2$ **h)** $4y - 8yz$ **i)** $6x + 12xy$ **j)** $10z + 20yz$
k) $12x + 24xyz$ **l)** $5x^2 + 10x$ **m)** $7x^2 + 21x$ **n)** $16x^2 + 8x$ **o)** $18y^2 - 9y$

Q18 Factorise:

a) $7a^2bc^2 + 14ab^2c + 21ab^2c^2 + 28a^2b^2c^2$
b) $100x^2yz + 90x^3yz + 80x^2y^2z + 70x^2yz + 60x^2yz^2$

Questions on Basic Algebra

It's all here — simplifying, multiplying out brackets and factorising.

How exciting.

Q19 Write using brackets:

a) $4x + 4y$
b) $16x + 8y$
c) $5x + 5y + 5z$
d) $14x + 7y$
e) $20x - 10y$
f) $3ax + 3ay$

Q20 What is the difference between $2a^2 + 3b^2 + 4a - b + 11$ and $a^2 + b^2 + 3a - 2b + 3$?

Q21 A flowerbed has length $(x + 10)$ m and width $(x + 4)$ m.

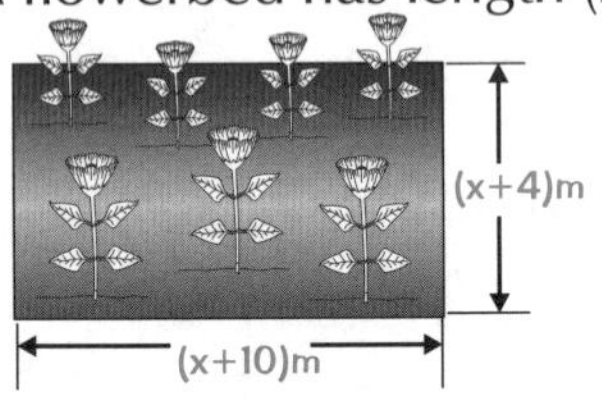

a) Write down and simplify an expression for the perimeter of the flowerbed.
b) Write down an expression for the area of the flowerbed and simplify it.

Q22 A rectangular bar of chocolate consists of 20 small rectangular pieces as shown. The size of a small rectangular piece of chocolate is 2 cm by x cm.

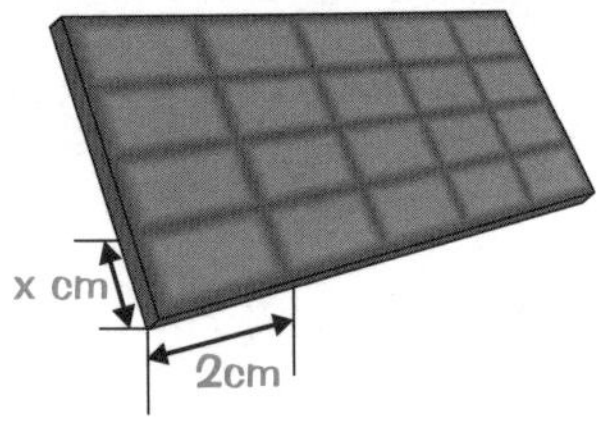

a) Write down an expression for the width of the whole bar.
b) Write down an expression for the perimeter of the whole bar.
c) Write down an expression for the area of the whole bar.
d) If I ate 6 small rectangular pieces of chocolate, what is the area of the remaining piece left over?

I'm not pretending these are all easy, but there's actually nothing new here. If you need to, check back over the last few pages for some top tips.

Q23 A bowling green has sides of length $(2x + 4)$ m.

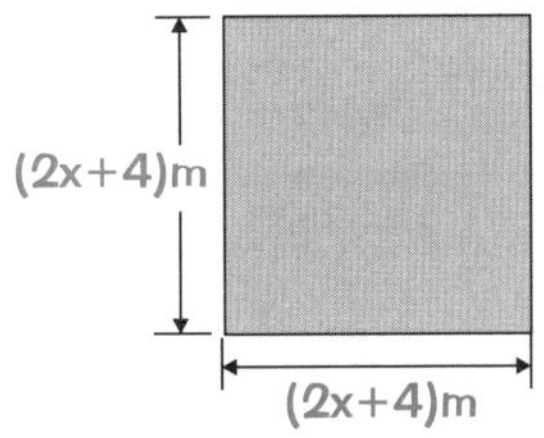

a) Write down an expression for the perimeter.
b) Write down an expression for the area and simplify it.
c) The bowling green needs a quarter of its area re-grassing, because of its poor condition. Write down an expression for the area of the bowling green which is still in good condition.

Q24 Remove the brackets and simplify where possible:

a) $14(x - 2y + z)$
b) $2(x - y) + 3(y - x)$
c) $3(4 + x) - (x - 2)$
d) $x^2(3 + 4x - 2xy)$
e) $2p(q + r) - 2q(p - r)$
f) $6x - (7 + 5x)$

Q25 Find a simplified expression for the area of each of the following shapes.

a)

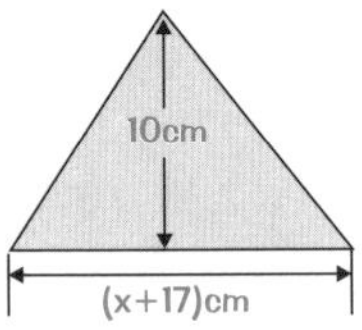

b)

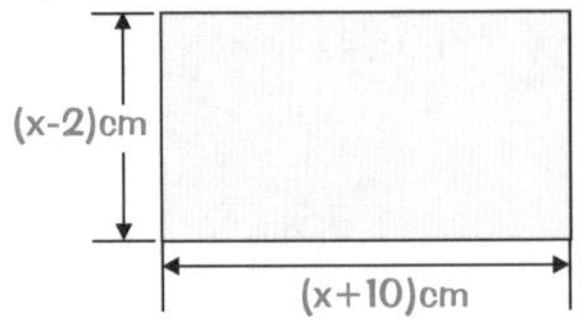

c)

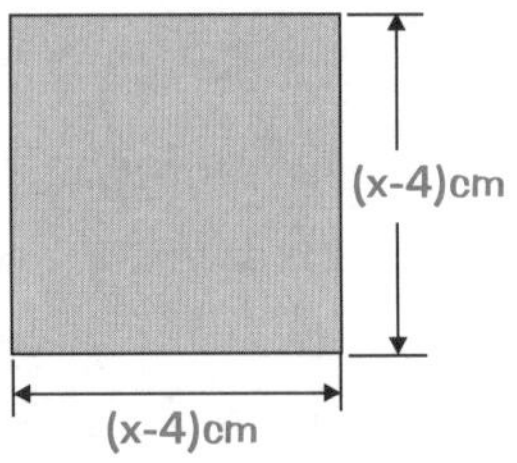

d)

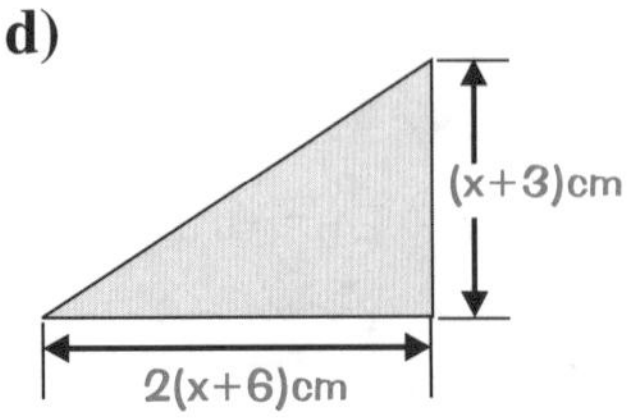

Q26 Find the product of $7x - 6$ and $2x + 3$.

Q27 Multiply $x + 2$ by $3x - 1$.

Q28 Find a simplified expression for

a) $(x + 1)^2$
b) $(x - 3)^2$
c) $(2x + 1)^2$

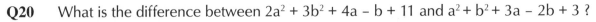

Remember $(x+1)^2$ is the same as $(x+1)(x+1)$.

Questions on Solving Equations

OK, so you've noticed this page starts off all right, but, things do get a bit hairy later on — so give yourself a head start by practising your algebra skills on the easy ones.

Q1 Solve the following:

a) $4x = 20$
b) $x + 3 = 11$
c) $x - 6 = 13$
d) $7x = -14$
e) $2x = -18$
f) $x + 5 = -3$
g) $x/2 = 22$
h) $x/7 = 3$
i) $2x + 1 = 7$
j) $2x + 4 = 5$
k) $7x + 5 = 54$
l) $6x - 7 = 41$

Q2 When eight is subtracted from a number the result is thirty-two.
a) Write this information as an equation.
b) Solve your equation to find the number.

Q3 When a number is multiplied by three and seven is added, the result is nineteen.
a) Write this information as an equation.
b) Solve your equation to find the number.

Q4 Andrew, Ben and Carl collect stamps. Andrew has 86 more than Ben and Carl has 156 more than Ben. If Ben has x stamps write down an expression for the number of stamps owned by:

a) Andrew
b) Carl
Altogether they have 776 stamps.
c) Using your previous answers write down and solve an equation in x.
d) How many stamps do Andrew and Carl have each?

Q5 Mary is y years old. Her father is 4 times older than Mary. Her mother is 7 years younger than her father. If their three ages add up to 101 years, find the value of y.
Find the ages of Mary's parents.

Q6 A girl spent t minutes on her Chemistry homework. She spent twice as long on her Maths homework, and her English homework took her 15 minutes longer than her Chemistry did. If she spent a total of 95 minutes working, find the value of t.

Q7 In a darts competition, Susan scored 147 more than John and three times as much as Elizabeth. If their combined score came to 336, find their individual scores.

Q8 Solve the following:

a) $3x - 4 = 2x + 4$
b) $3x - 8 = 5x - 20$
c) $23 - x = x + 11$
d) $2(x - 3) - (x - 2) = 5$
e) $2x - 5 = \frac{1}{2}x + 4$
f) $3(x + 1) = 9$

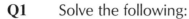

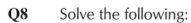

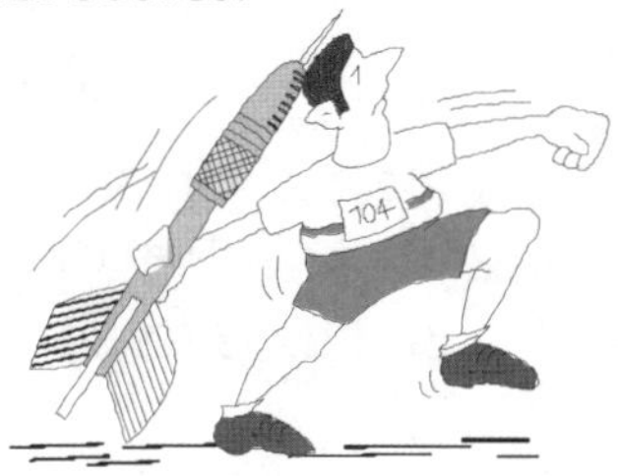

Q9 Solve the following:

a) $3(7 - 2x) = 2(5 - 4x)$
b) $6(x + 2) + 4(x - 3) = 50$
c) $2(4x - 12) = 6(3x - 4)$
d) $2(2x - 1) = 3(4x + 2)$
e) $5(x + 3) = 4(2x - 5)$
f) $2(2x + 3) + 5(3x + 1) = 6(3x + 4)$
g) $4(3x + 2) + 3 = 3(2x - 5) + 2$
h) $10(x + 3) - 4(x - 2) = 7(x + 5)$
i) $5(4x + 3) = 4(7x - 5) + 3(9 - 2x)$
j) $3(7 + 2x) + 2(1 - x) = 19$

Questions on Solving Equations

Well, the good thing about doing all of these is that soon you'll be able to do algebra with your eyes closed. That'll be nice.

Q10 Find x in the following:

a) $x/2 + 4 = 7$
b) $8 + x/3 = 11$
c) $20 + x/4 = 22$
d) $x/3 + 7 = 12$
e) $x/10 + 18 = 29$
f) $5 - x/2 = 3$
g) $10 - x/3 = 1$
h) $50 - x/4 = 18$
i) $17 - x/3 = 5$
j) $41 - x/11 = 35$
k) $2x/5 = 4$
l) $3x/4 = 75$
m) $2x/3 = 14$
n) $x/100 = 5$
o) $x/100 - 3 = 4$
p) $40/x = 8$
q) $55/x = 11$
r) $200/x = 25$
s) $120/x = 16$
t) $90/x = 20$

Q11 The angles of a quadrilateral add up to 360°. Form an equation in x and solve it for each of the following shapes:

a)
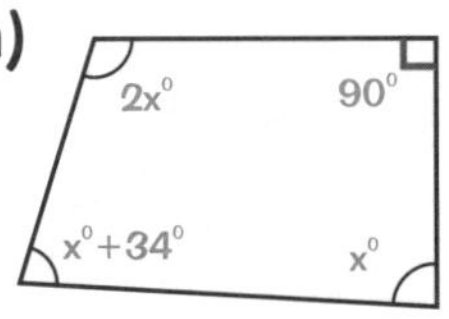

b)
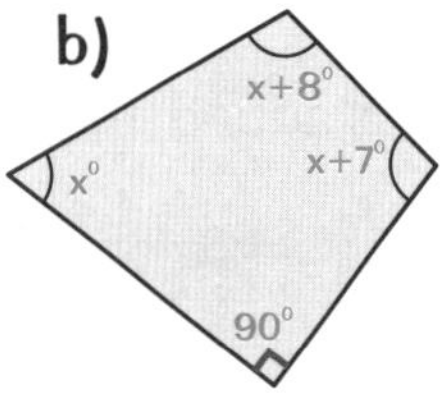

c)
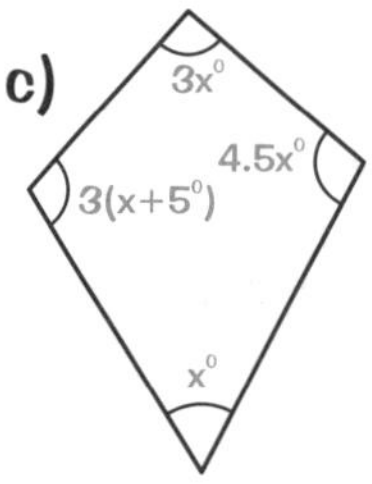

d)
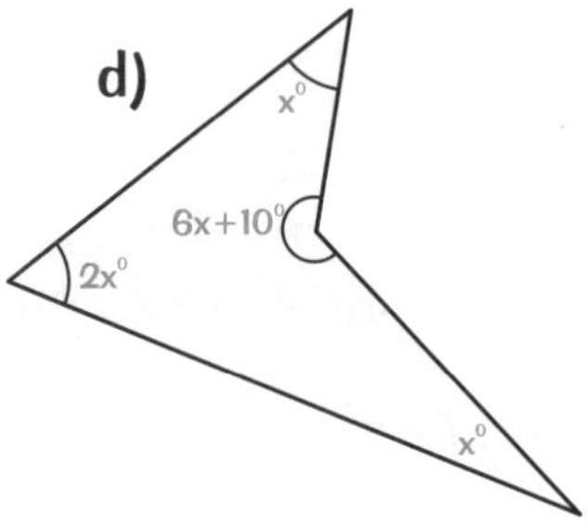

Q12 Joan, Kate and Linda win £2400 between them on the National Lottery. Joan gets a share of £x, whilst Kate gets twice as much as Joan. Linda's share is £232 less than Joan's amount.

a) Write down an expression for the amounts Joan, Kate and Linda win.
b) Write down an equation in x, and solve it.
c) Write down the amounts Kate and Linda receive.

Q13 Solve the following:–

a) $8m - \frac{1}{2} = 6m + 7$
b) $\frac{1}{2}p - 13 = 3p + 7$
c) $\frac{3}{4}t + 6 = \frac{1}{4}t + 8$
d) $\frac{1}{2}z + 2 = \frac{1}{4}z + 6$

Get rid of any unwanted fractions by multiplying the whole equation by the bottom number. If you've got a couple of fractions with different numbers at the bottom, multiply by their LCM (see P.17).

Don't forget to multiply each term by the same thing or things'll go a bit pear-shaped.

Q14 For what value of x is the expression $14 - 0.5x$ equal to the value $(3x - 4)/2$?

Q15 Solve the following:

a) $4x + 2x + 20 = 62$
b) $4(x - 2) = 16$
c) $3(x + 2) = 21$
d) $6(x + 3) - (x - 2) = 60$
e) $4(x - 1) - 2(3 - x) = 50$
f) $2(4 - x) - (x + 2) = 28$

Q16 I think of a number, multiply it by 8 and add 13. The result is one less than the original number. What number did I start with?

Q17 Carol's father was 24 yrs old when Carol was born. Now he is four times as old as Carol. How old is Carol?

Q18 Mr Jones is 4 years older than his wife and 31 years older than his son. Their ages add up to 82 years. If Mr Jones is x years old, find the value of x and find all their ages.

Questions on Substituting Values

BODMAS — this funny little word helps you remember in which order to work formulas out. The example below shows you how to use it. Oh and by the way "Other" might not seem important, but it means things like powers, square and cube roots, etc — so it is.

Brackets, Other, Division, Multiplication, Addition, Subtraction

Example: if $z = \frac{x}{10} + (y-3)^2$ find the value of z when x = 40 and y = 13.

1) Write down the formula with the numbers substituted in,

$$z = \frac{40}{10} + (13-3)^2$$

2) Brackets first $\quad z = \frac{40}{10} + (10)^2$

3) Other next, so square $\quad z = \frac{40}{10} + 100$

4) Division before Addition $\quad z = 4 + 100$

$\underline{z = 104}$

Q1 If x = 3 and y = 6 find the value of the following expressions.

a) $x + 2y$ **c)** $4(x + y)$ **e)** $2x^2$

b) $2x \div y$ **d)** $(y - x)^2$ **f)** $2y^2$

Q2 The cost of framing a picture, C pence, depends on the dimensions of the picture. If C = 10L + 5W, where L is the length in cm and W is the width in cm, then find the cost of framing

a) a picture 40 cm by 24 cm

b) a square picture of sides 30 cm.

Q3 Using the formula $z = (x - 10)^2$, find the value of z when,

a) x = 20

b) x = 15

c) x = -1

Use the memory button on your calc, so you don't have to keep typing things in yourself.

Q4 If $V = \pi r^2 h$ find the value of V when r = 4 and h = 6. Take $\pi = 3.14$.

Q5 In a Physics experiment two resistors of strengths P and Q are connected in an electrical circuit and their total resistance R ohms is given by $R = \frac{PQ}{P+Q}$.

Find the total resistance of the circuit when

a) P = 3 and Q = 3

b) P = 60 and Q = 40.

You don't need to know anything about Physics for this — just worry about the equation, rather than what it stands for.

Q6 The time taken to cook a chicken is given as 20 minutes per lb plus 20 minutes extra. Find the time needed to cook a chicken weighing

a) 4 lb

b) 7.5 lb.

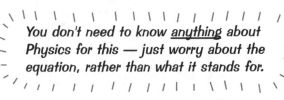

Questions on Rearranging Formulas

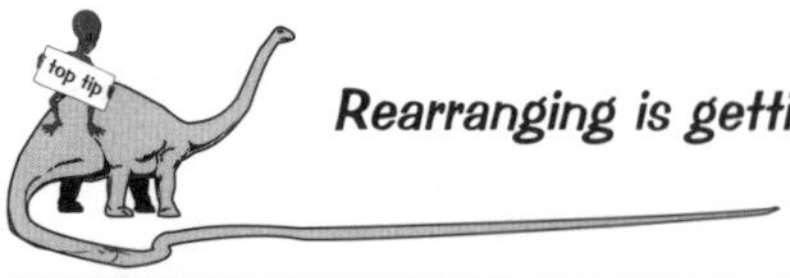

Rearranging is getting the letter you want out of the formula and making it the subject.

Example:- Rearrange the formula $p = 3q + r$ to make q the subject.

$$p = 3q + r$$
$$p - r = 3q$$
$$\frac{p-r}{3} = q$$
$$q = \frac{p-r}{3}$$

Subtract r from each side

Divide by 3

Rewrite starting with new subject

Remember
The same method applies to rearranging formulas as solving equations

Q1 Rearrange the following formulas to make the letter in brackets the new subject:

a) $y = x + 4$ ....(x) **d)** $y = 3x + ½$ .....(x) **g)** $x = 8 - 3z$ ....(z) **j)** $a = 3(b - 2)$ ....(b)
b) $y = 2x + 3$ ....(x) **e)** $p = 4 - q$ ....(q) **h)** $g = 10 - 4h$ ......(h) **k)** $d = ½(c + 4)$ ......(c)
c) $y = 4x - 5$ ....(x) **f)** $f = 12 - g$ ....(g) **i)** $y = 5(x + 2)$ ......(x) **l)** $g = -(h + 2)$ ....(h)

Q2 Rearrange the following, to make the letter in brackets the subject of the formulas:

a) $y = \frac{x}{10}$ ....(x) **c)** $a = \frac{2b}{3}$ ....(b) **e)** $f = \frac{3g}{8}$ ....(g) **g)** $y = \frac{x}{2} - 3$ ......(x)

b) $s = \frac{t}{14}$ ....(t) **d)** $d = \frac{3e}{4}$ ....(e) **f)** $y = \frac{x}{5} + 1$ ...(x) **h)** $a = \frac{b}{3} - 5$ .....(b)

Q3 The cost of hiring a spacetaxi is £28 for each whole light year plus 25p per extra mile. (A light year is the distance light travels in a year. So it's very large.)

a) Find the cost of hiring the spacetaxi and travelling
i) 1 light year and 40 miles **ii)** 1 light year and 80 miles
b) Write down a formula to give £c the cost of hiring a spacetaxi, in pounds, for travelling one light year and n miles.
c) Rearrange the formula to make n the subject.
d) What is the furthest you can travel on this amount of money?
i) £34 **ii)** £50 **iii)** £56.50

Q4 Rearrange the following formulas to make the letter in brackets the new subject.

a) $y = x^2$ ....(x) **e)** $a = \sqrt{b} - 2$ ....(b) **i)** $p = (3q)^2$ ....(q)
b) $p = 4q^2$ ....(q) **f)** $y = \sqrt{x+3}$ ....(x)
c) $y = x^2 - 2$ ....(x) **g)** $s = (t - 3)^2$ ....(t) **j)** $r = \left(\frac{s}{2}\right)^2$ ....(s)
d) $y = (2x)^2$ ....(x) **h)** $y = \sqrt{x}$ ....(x) **k)** $a = \frac{b-2}{3}$ ....(b)

Q5 The cost of developing a film is 12p per print plus 60p postage.

a) Find the cost of developing a film with **i)** 12 prints **ii)** 24 prints.
b) Write down a formula for the cost C, in pence, of developing x prints.
c) Rearrange the formula to make x the subject.
d) Find the number of prints developed when a customer is charged
i) £4.92 **ii)** £6.36 **iii)** £12.12.

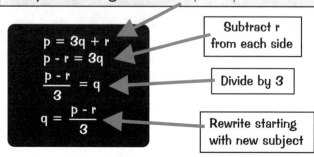

Questions on Quadratics

It's factorising Jim, but not as we know it... Better watch out with these, I reckon.

Factorising Quadratics

1) A QUADRATIC expression is of the form $[x^2 + bx + c]$
2) FACTORISING a quadratic expression means putting it into two brackets.

Eg: Factorising $x^2 - 2x - 8$ will give $(x - 4)(x + 2)$.

To check this works, multiply out again, using FOIL:

$$(x - 4)(x + 2) = x^2 + 2x - 4x - 8$$
$$= x^2 - 2x - 8$$

-8 = -1 x 8
-8 x 1
-2 x 4
-4 x 2

(x)(x)

To complete the brackets find two numbers which multiply to give c, and at the same time either + or - to give b. Finally put in +or - signs, checking that the two brackets will multiply out to give the equation.

Q1 Factorise the following equations:

a) $x^2 + 3x + 2$
b) $x^2 + 5x + 6$
c) $x^2 + 8x + 15$
d) $x^2 + 7x + 10$
e) $x^2 + 12x + 27$
f) $x^2 + 15x + 36$
g) $x^2 + 10x + 24$
h) $x^2 + 11x + 24$
i) $x^2 + 12x + 36$

Your best bet with Q1 is the old guessing game. Come up with a pair of numbers, then try adding and multiplying them.

Remember, they've got to multiply together to make the number at the end and add together to make the x term in the middle. Think of FOIL...

Q2 Factorise each of the following:

a) $x^2 + 3x$
b) $x^2 + 8x$
c) $x^2 + 10x$
d) $x^2 - 4x$
e) $x^2 - 8x$
f) $x^2 - 20x$
g) $2x - x^2$
h) $5x - x^2$
i) $9x - x^2$

Q2 is a bit like the ones from P.41. These are quadratics, though, so you can still factorise them in the same way.

Q3 Factorise the following:

a) $x^2 + x - 6$
b) $x^2 - x - 12$
c) $x^2 - 2x - 35$
d) $x^2 - 4x - 32$
e) $x^2 - 3x - 54$
f) $x^2 - 5x + 6$
g) $x^2 - 6x + 8$
h) $x^2 - 11x + 30$
i) $x^2 - 13x + 30$
j) $x^2 - 11x + 28$
k) $x^2 - 3x - 40$
l) $x^2 + 10x - 24$

Q4 Factorise the following using the difference of two squares:

a) $x^2 - 9$
b) $x^2 - 64$
c) $4x^2 - 36$
d) $9x^2 - 100$
e) $x^2 - y^2$
f) $16x^2 - 25y^2$

I've seen the sign... when you get any negative numbers in there, look at where the signs are and think about your sign rules for multiplying — it'll help you work out the signs of the numbers you're looking for. Which is bound to save time.

Q5 Factorise the quadratic expression $x^2 + 90x - 1000$.

Questions on Quadratics

We're solving them now — but it's OK, it's only an (easy) step on from factorising.

Solving Quadratic Equations

1) A <u>QUADRATIC EQUATION</u> is usually of the form $[x^2 + bx + c = 0]$
2) It can be factorised to give $(x \pm ?)(x \pm ?) = 0$
3) To find the <u>two</u> answers <u>either</u> the <u>first</u> bracket must equal zero, <u>or</u> the <u>second</u> bracket must <u>equal zero</u>.

Eg: Solve $x^2 - 4x = 21$:

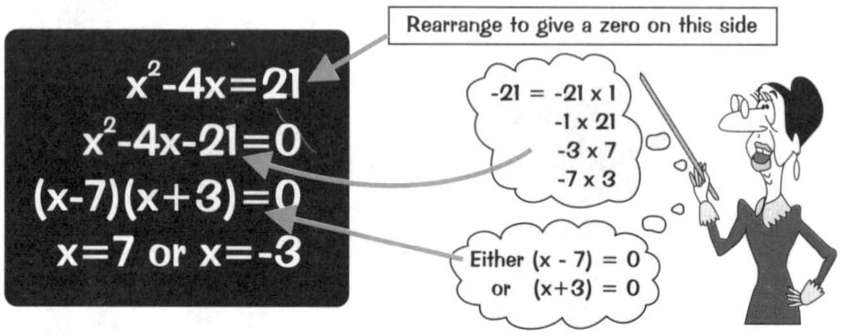

Rearrange to give a zero on this side
x²-4x=21
x²-4x-21=0
(x-7)(x+3)=0
x=7 or x=-3
-21 = -21 x 1
-1 x 21
-3 x 7
-7 x 3
Either (x - 7) = 0
or (x+3) = 0

Q6 Solve the following quadratic equations:

a) $(x + 4)(x - 3) = 0$
b) $(x + 2)(x + 8) = 0$
c) $(x - 1)(x - 7) = 0$
d) $(x + 4)^2 = 0$
e) $(x - 25)^2 = 0$
f) $x(x - 7) = 0$
g) $x(x + 30) = 0$
h) $(3 - x)(4 - x) = 0$

For the ones where you get one bracket squared, eg $(x + 1)^2 = 0$, there's only the one answer (Which is $x = -1$, in this case).

Q7 Find x by solving the following quadratic equations:

a) $x^2 + 6x + 8 = 0$
b) $x^2 + 3x - 10 = 0$
c) $x^2 - 6x + 9 = 0z$
d) $x^2 - 2x + 1 = 0$
e) $x^2 - 3x - 18 = 0$
f) $x^2 - 4x + 3 = 0$
g) $x^2 - 4x - 5 = 0$
h) $x^2 + 9x + 8 = 0$
i) $x^2 + 6x - 7 = 0$

(Don't forget you've got to factorise before you start solving.)

Q8 Rearrange into the form $x^2 + bx + c = 0$, then solve by factorising:

a) $x^2 - 2x = 15$
b) $x^2 + 5x = 14$
c) $x^2 + 6x = 16$
d) $x^2 = 5x$
e) $x^2 = 7x$
f) $x^2 = 11x$
g) $x^2 - 300 = 20x$
h) $x^2 + 48 = 26x$
i) $x^2 + 36 = 13x$

Q9 David is 3 years younger than his sister Jane.

a) If David is x years old, write down Jane's age as an expression containing x.
b) If the product of David and Jane's age is 130, use **a)** to form an <u>equation involving x</u> and then solve it.
c) How old is David?

Q10

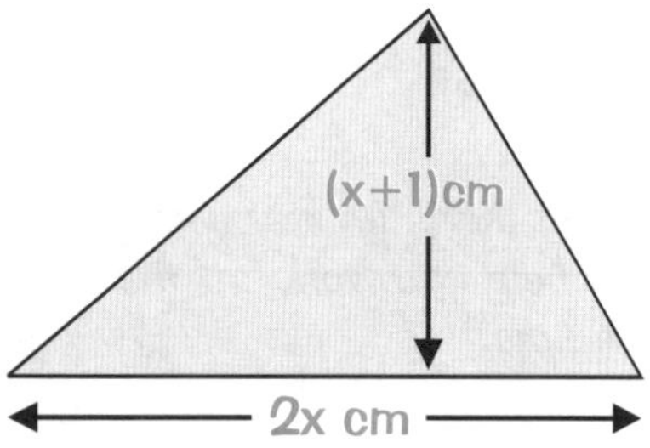

A triangle has height $(x + 1)$ cm and a base of $2x$ cm.

a) Write down an expression for <u>half of its base</u>.
b) Write down an expression for the area of the triangle and simplify it.
c) If the area of the triangle is equal to 12 cm^2, write down a quadratic equation using your answer to part **b)**.
d) Solve this quadratic equation to find the value of x.

Questions on Trial and Improvement

Well, OK this one's a bit boring, but at least it's reliable — it doesn't depend on your drawing for a start...

Solving a Cubic Equation

Eg The cubic equation $x^3 + 2x = 15$ has a solution between 2 and 3. Find this to 1 d.p.

Guess (x)	value of x^3+2x	Too large or too small
2	$2^3+2(2)=12$	Too small
3	$3^3+2(3)=33$	Too large
2.3	$(2.3)^3+2(2.3)=16.767$	Too large
2.2	$(2.2)^3+2(2.2)=15.048$	Too large ...Just!
2.1	$(2.1)^3+2(2.1)=13.461$	Too small
2.15	$(2.15)^3+2(2.15)=14.238$	Too small

2 gave an answer closer to 15 so the next guess should be nearer to 2 than 3.

In this example it looks like x=2.2, but to be totally sure, always try exactly halfway when you reach this stage.

∴ To 1 d.p the solution is <u>x=2.2</u>

Q1 The cubic equation $x^3 + x = 24$ has a solution between 2 and 3.
Copy and complete the table below and use it to find this solution to <u>1 DP</u>.

Guess (x)	value of x^3+x	Too large or too small
2	$2^3+2=$	
3	$3^3+3=$	

Extend the table as necessary

Q2 The cubic equation $x^3 - x = 34$ has a solution between 3 and 4.
Copy and complete the table below and use it to find this solution to <u>1 DP</u>.

Guess (x)	value of $x^3 - x$	Too large or too small
3	$3^3 - 3=$	
4	$4^3 - 4=$	

Q3 The cubic equation $3x - x^3 = 20$ has a solution between −4 and −3.
Copy and complete the table below and use it to find this solution to <u>1 DP</u>.

Guess (x)	value of $3x-x^3$	Too large or too small
-4	$3(-4)-(-4)^3=52$	
-3	$3(-3)-(-3)^3=$	

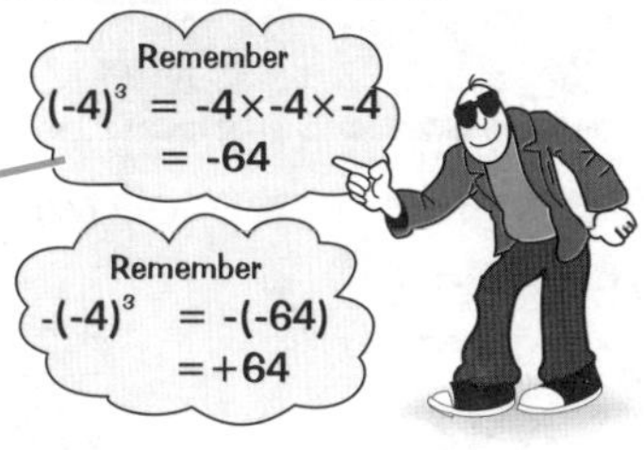
Remember
$(-4)^3 = -4\times-4\times-4$
$= -64$
Remember
$-(-4)^3 = -(-64)$
$= +64$

Q4 The cubic equation $2x^3 - x^2 = 50$ has a solution between 3 and 4.
Use the table to find this solution to <u>1 DP</u>.

Guess (x)	value of $2x^3 - x^2$	Too large or too small
3	$2(3)^3 - (3)^2 =$	
4	$2(4)^3 - (4)^2 =$	

Questions on Simultaneous Equations

The name makes it sound scary, but these are just 2 equations with the same solutions.

To solve simultaneous equations from scratch, you've got to get rid of either x or y first — to leave you with an equation with just one unknown in it. You do this by adding or subtracting equations — have a look at this example:

Eg: solve the simultaneous equations $2x + 3y = 13$ and $2x - y = 1$.	
1) There is a 2x in both equations, so eliminate x by subtracting one equation from the other:	$(2x - 2x) + (3y - {}^-y) = (13 - 1)$, so $4y = 12$ hence $y = 3$
2) Then substitute $y = 3$ back into either equation, to find x:	$2x + 9 = 13$ $2x = 13 - 9 = 4$ hence $x = 2$

Q1 Use the above example as a guide to solve the following pairs of equations:

a) $3x + y = 7$, $2x - y = 3$
b) $x + y = 12$, $x - y = 2$
c) $x + 3y = 10$, $2x - 3y = 2$
d) $10x - 2y = -8$, $10x + y = 19$
e) $2x + 7y = 11$, $2x + 3y = 7$
f) $5x - 3y = -2$, $-5x + y = 4$

Q2 Rearrange one of the equations before eliminating either the x term or y term by adding or subtracting the pair of equations, then solve:

a) $3y - 4x = 10$, $4x - 2y = -8$
b) $3x + y = 13$, $2y - 3x = 8$
c) $y + 1 = 3x$, $y - x = 3$
d) $y + x = 2$, $y - \frac{1}{2}x + 1 = 0$
e) $y = 5 - 2x$, $y = x - 4$
f) $6x + 2y = 5$, $3y - 6x = 15$

Multiply one equation by a number before adding or subtracting. Solve the equations.

eg. Solve $3x + y = 17$ ...... (A)
$4x - 2y = 36$ .... (B)

Multiplying (A) by 2, then adding
$6x + 2y = 34$
$+\ 4x - 2y = 36$
$10x = 70$
$x = 7$

SUB INTO (A)

$3(7) + y = 17$
$21 + y = 17$
$y = -4$

Remember
When you multiply an equation by 2 every term in that equation doubles.
When you multiply an equation by 3 every term in that equation trebles.

The first thing you've got to do is label the equations A and B.

Remember
Always substitute your first answer back into an original equation to find the second answer.
There is less chance of making a mistake this way.

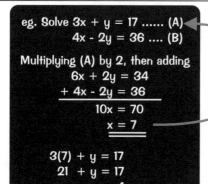

Q3 Find x and y in the following:

a) $3x + 2y = 12$, $2x + y = 7$
b) $5x - y = 17$, $2x + 3y = 0$
c) $3x + 2y = 3$, $2x + y = 23$
d) $4x + 2y = 8$, $x + 3y = 2$
e) $6x - y = -4$, $3x - 2y = 1$
f) $5x - 4y = 7$, $7x - 2y = 17$
g) $8x - y = 6$, $7x + 5y = 17$
h) $8x + 3y = 27$, $2x - 5y = 1$

Q4 Multiply both equations by a number before adding or subtracting to solve these equations:

a) $3x + 2y = 13$, $2x + 3y = 7$
b) $4x + 2y = 10$, $7x + 3y = 16$
c) $6x - 3y = 3$, $5x - 2y = 4$
d) $7x - 3y = 18$, $5x + 2y = 17$
e) $7y - 3x = 2$, $5y - 2x = 2$
f) $5x - 8y = 12$, $4x - 7y = 9$
g) $7x + 5y = 66$, $3x - 4y = 16$
h) $10x + 4y = 2$, $8x + 3y = 1$

Questions on Simultaneous Equations

It's DIY time — you've got to write your own equations, and then solve them. Not asking for much...

Q5 Two numbers x and y have a <u>sum</u> of 15 and a <u>difference</u> of 3.

a) Write a pair of simultaneous equations in x and y.

b) Solve for x and y.

Q6 Two numbers x and y have a sum of 4 and a difference of 12. Find the values of x and y.

(<u>Hint — one is negative.</u>)

Q7 A farmer has a choice of buying 6 sheep and 5 pigs for £430 <u>or</u> 4 sheep and 10 pigs for £500 at auction.

a) If sheep cost £x and pigs cost £y, write down his <u>two choices</u> as a pair of simultaneous equations.

b) Solve for x and y.

Q8 Six apples and four oranges cost £1.90, whereas eight apples and two oranges cost £1.80. Find the cost of an apple and the cost of an orange.

Q9 Find the value of x and y for each of the following rectangles, by first writing down a pair of simultaneous equations and then solving them.

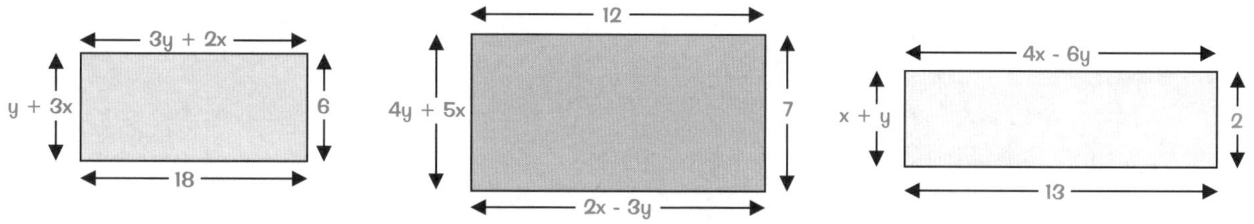

Q10 Two groups of people place two orders in a café. The first group orders 4 cups of coffee and 2 cups of tea and their bill is for £4.80. The second group orders 3 cups of coffee and 5 cups of tea and their bill is for £6.05.

a) Write down two simultaneous equations involving a cup of coffee (c) and a cup of tea (t).

b) Find the value of c and t, <u>in pence</u>.

Q11 A box has length (x + y) cm, height (y + 4) cm and width 2x cm, where the length is 12 cm and the height is 11 cm.

a) Write down a pair of simultaneous equations involving x and y.

b) Solve the simultaneous equations to find the value of x and y.

c) By substituting in your value of x, find the <u>volume</u> of the cube in cm^3.

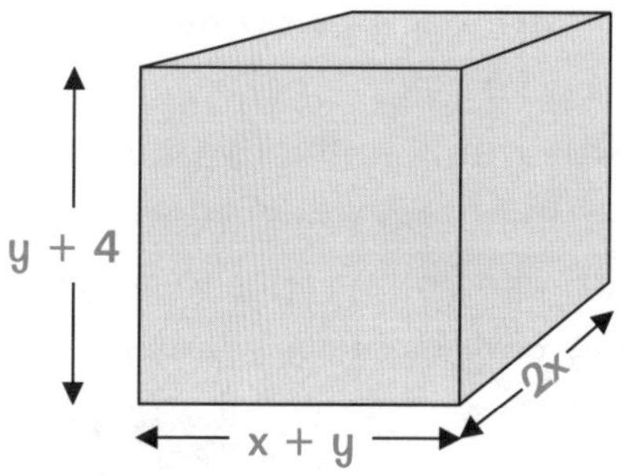

Q12

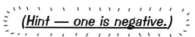

Two customers enter a shop to buy milk and cornflakes. Mrs Smith buys 5 pints of milk and 2 boxes of cornflakes and spends £3.44. Mr Brown buys 4 pints of milk and 3 boxes of cornflakes and receives £6.03 <u>change</u> after paying with a £10 note. Write down a pair of simultaneous equations and solve them to find the price in pence of a pint of milk (m) and a box of cornflakes (c).

Questions on Simultaneous Eq' Graphs

The solution of two simultaneous equations is simply the X and Y values where their graphs cross

1) Simultaneous equations can be plotted as two straight-line graphs on the same axes.
2) The point where the lines cross will have coordinates equal to the values of x and y which satisfy both equations.

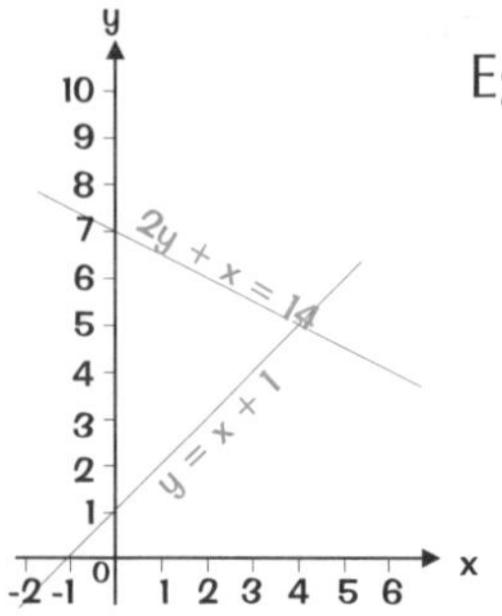

Eg: Solve:
$y = x + 1$
$2y + x = 14$

The two lines intersect where $x = 4$ and $y = 5$, so this is the solution.

Q1 Solve these simultaneous equations by looking at the graphs. Then check your answers by substituting the values back into the equations.

a) $y + 2x = 9$
$3y = x + 6$

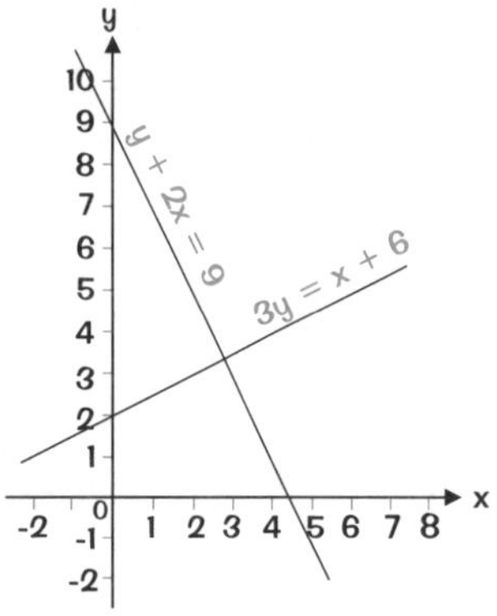

b) $y = 2x - 13$
$2y + x + 6 = 0$

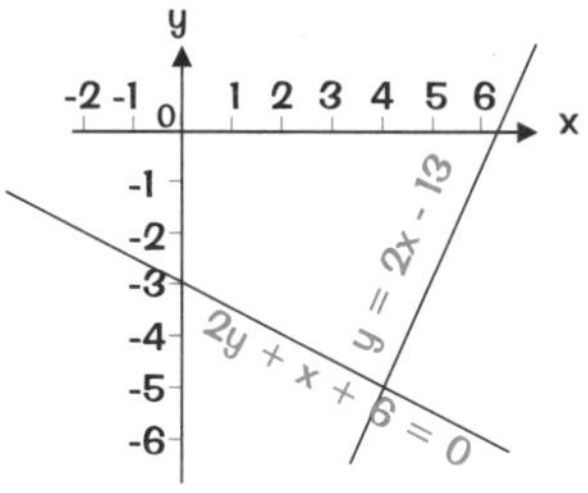

This is a nice easy way of solving simultaneous equations. You don't need to do all those steps that can make the other method a little bit tricky. All you have to be able to do is draw two straight line graphs and read off a value where they cross each other. That means you've got to be up to speed with your straight line graphs, though...

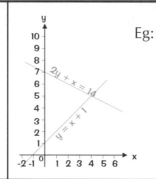

For each pair of simultaneous equations below:
a) draw and label a pair of axes with x from –3 to 7, and y from –6 to 6
b) complete the two tables of values
c) plot two straight-line graphs onto your axes, remembering to label each graph
d) use your graphs to find the value of x and y
e) check your answers by substituting them into both of the equations.

Q2 $y = x + 2$
$y = 3x - 2$

x	–2	0	4
y = x+2	0	2	

x	0	1	2
y = 3x–2	–2		

Q3 $y = 2x - 2$
$2y = x + 8$

x			
y = 2x-2			

x			
y = ½x+4			

Q4 $y = 2 - x$
$y = \frac{1}{2}x - 1$

x			
y = 2-x			

x			
y = ½x–1			

Questions on Quadratic Graphs

You can write all quadratic graphs in this form — though you probably won't see the point of doing it 'till you've done quite a few of them. Hang in there.

The simplest quadratic graph is $y = x^2$

x	-4	-3	-2	-1	0	1	2	3	4
y	16	9	4	1	0	1	4	9	16

$y=ax^2+bx+c$

There will always be an x^2 term. The value of 'a' can not be zero

Sometimes either 'b' or 'c' could be zero. Even if both were equal to zero, the graph would still be quadratic

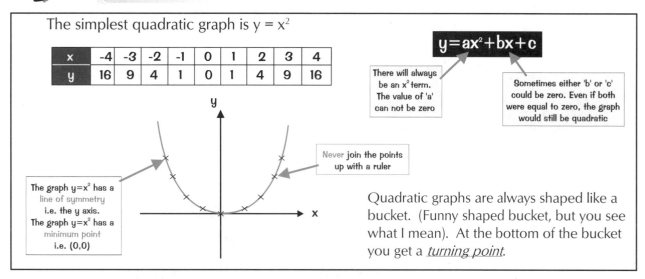

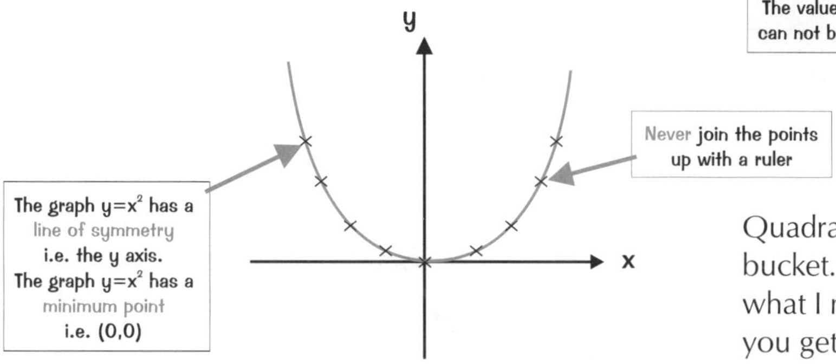

y
x
The graph y=x² has a line of symmetry i.e. the y axis.
The graph y=x² has a minimum point i.e. (0,0)
Never join the points up with a ruler

Quadratic graphs are always shaped like a bucket. (Funny shaped bucket, but you see what I mean). At the bottom of the bucket you get a *turning point*.

Q1 Complete this table of values for the quadratic graph $y = 2x^2$.

a) Draw axes with x from -4 to 4 and y from 0 to 32.

b) Plot these 9 points and join them with a smooth curve.

c) Label your graph.

x	-4	-3	-2	-1	0	1	2	3	4
$y=2x^2$	32	18					8		

Remember to square first then x 2

You always get a vertical line of symmetry down the middle of the graph, and you can often be asked to write its equation down. Remember that a vertical line will always have the equation "x = something", the something being the number where it crosses the x-axis. (Have a quick look back at P.53 of The Revision Guide)

Q2 Complete this table of values for the graph $y = x^2 + x$.

x	-4	-3	-2	-1	0	1	2	3	4
x^2	16	9					8		
$y=x^2+x$	12					2			

By putting more steps in your table of values, the arithmetic is easier

a) Draw axes with x from -4 to 4 and y from 0 to 20.

b) Plot the points and join them with a smooth curve.

c) Draw the line of symmetry for the quadratic graph $y = x^2 + x$, and label it.

d) Describe the turning point of the quadratic and state its coordinates.

If the x^2 term has a minus sign in front of it, the bucket will be turned upside down.

Q3 **a)** Draw the graph $y = -x^2$ for values of x from -4 to 4.

b) Describe the turning point of the graph and state its coordinates.

c) How are this graph and the graph $y = x^2$ (at the top of this page) related?

If you don't get the equation given in the form $y = ax^2 + bx + c$ then put it in that form first. You'll get in a right mess if you don't.

Questions on Quadratic Graphs

It's handy to know whether a quadratic graph will have a <u>maximum point</u> or a <u>minimum point</u> without having to plot the graph first. This is how you know:

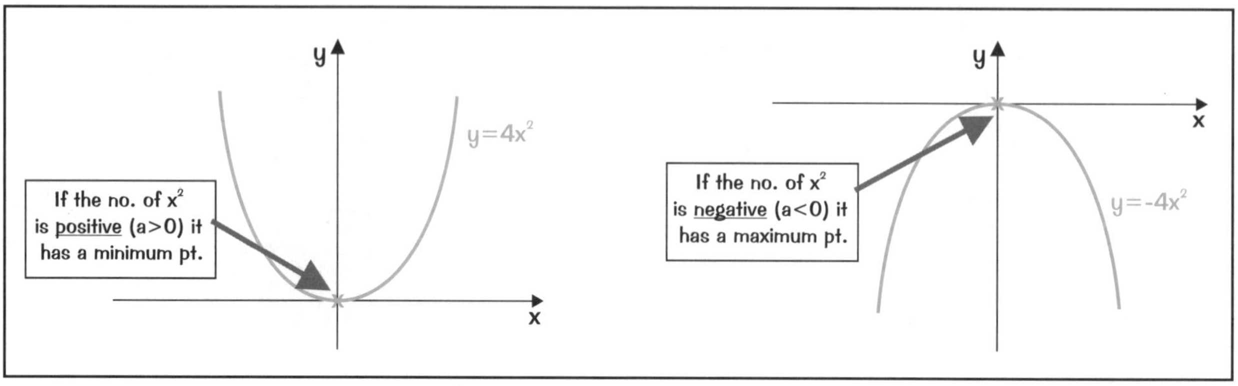

(If the bucket is the right way up, you get a minimum. If it's upside down, you get a maximum.)

Q4 **a)** Complete this table of values for the graph $y = 3 - x^2$.

b) Draw the graph $y = 3 - x^2$ for x from -4 to 4.

c) State the <u>maximum point</u> of the graph $y = 3 - x^2$.

d) State the <u>maximum value</u> of the graph $y = 3 - x^2$.

x	-4	-3	-2	-1	0	1	2	3	4
3	3	3	3	3	3	3	3	3	3
$-x^2$	-16						-4		
$y=3-x^2$	-13						-1		

If you don't get a smooth curve you've screwed up.

Q5 **a)** Complete this table of values for the graph $y = x^2 - 4x + 1$.

b) <u>Plot the graph</u> $y = x^2 - 4x + 1$, using axes with x from -2 to 4 and y from -3 to 13.

c) Draw and label the <u>line of symmetry</u>.

d) What is the minimum value of the graph $y = x^2 - 4x + 1$?

x	-2	-1	0	1	2	3	4
x^2	4	1				9	
$-4x$	8					-12	
1	1	1				1	
$y=x^2-4x+1$	13	6				-2	

Q6 <u>Without drawing their graphs</u>, determine whether these quadratic graphs will have maximum points or minimum points.

a) $y = 2x^2 - 5$

b) $y = 10 - x^2$

c) $y = 4x - 3x^2$

d) $y = 5 - 3x + x^2$.

Q7 **a)** Draw axes with x from -3 to 5 and y from -9 to 7.

b) By first completing the table of values, plot the graph $y = x^2 - 2x - 8$.

c) State the line of symmetry.

d) <u>Describe the turning point</u> and state its coordinates.

x	
x^2	
$-2x$	
-8	
$y=x^2-2x-8$	

If any points look a bit strange, check you've got them right in the <u>table of values</u>. I know it's boring doing it all again, but it shouldn't be too hard if you've put all the steps in. And it'll mean you <u>don't get it wrong</u>. Which is always nice.

Questions on Solving Eq's with Graphs

Finding solutions to equations

a) $x^2 - 2x = 0$, so $x = 0$ or $x = 2$

Solve $x^2 - 2x = 0$ by looking at the $y = 0$ line ie. where the graph cuts the x axis

x	-2	-1	0	1	2	3
x^2	4	1	0	1	4	9
$-2x$	4	2	0	-2	-4	-6
$y=x^2-2x$	8	3	0	-1	0	3

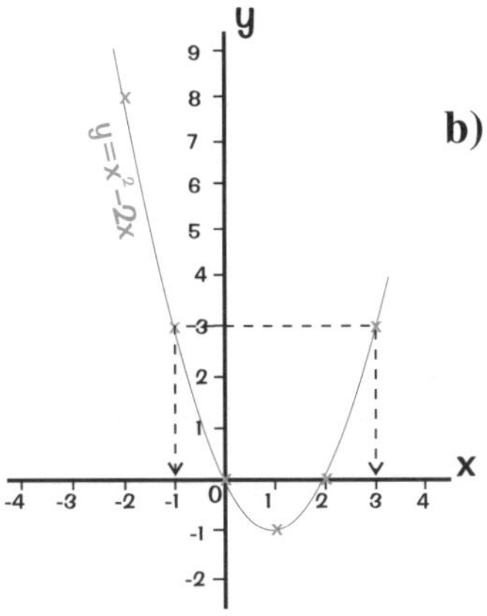

b) $x^2 - 2x = 3$, so $x = -1$ or $x = 3$

Solve $x^2 - 2x = 3$ by drawing a line across from the y axis at $y = 3$. Where it hits the curve, follow down to the x axis. Read off the x values.

Write down the solutions of the quadratic equations by reading them from the graphs below. Check your answers by substituting them into the equations.

Q1 Solve:

a) $3x - x^2 = 0$ and
b) $3x - x^2 = 2$

c) $x^2 - 2x + 1 = 0$ and
d) $x^2 - 2x + 1 = 4$

e) $x^2 - 6x + 5 = 0$ and
f) $x^2 - 6x + 5 = -3$

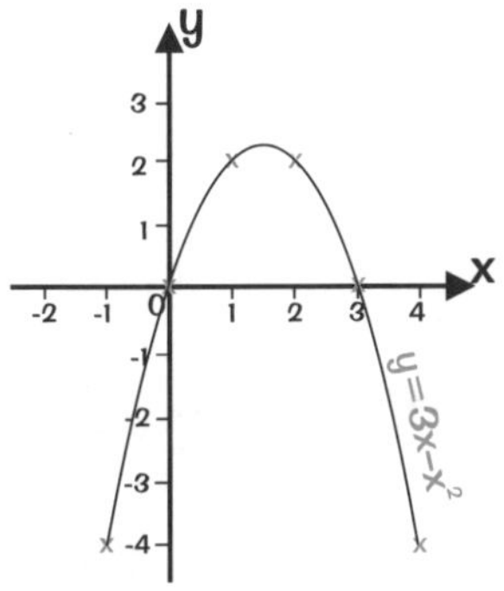

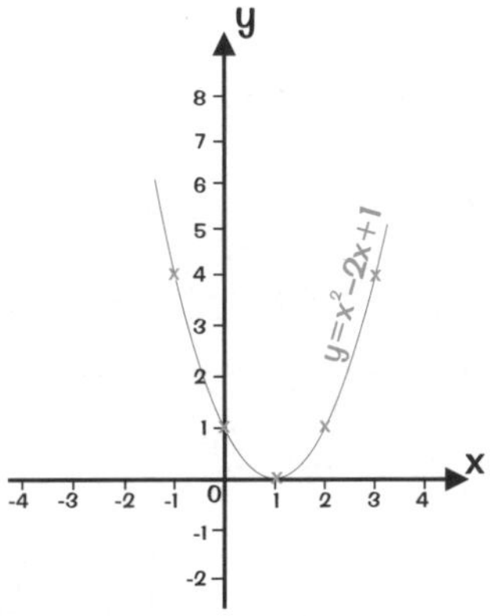

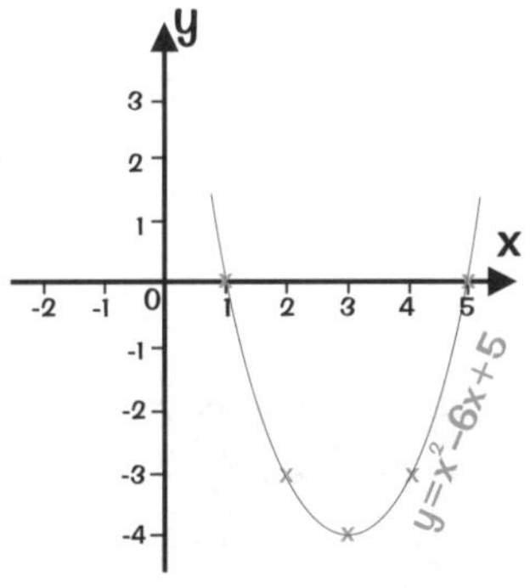

You'll need quite a good graph with a nice smooth curve to solve these equations, so be as neat as you can with your plotting. If you don't draw it carefully, then the line won't cross the axis in the right place and your answer won't be right either.

Q2 **a)** Complete the table of values for the quadratic graph $y = x^2 - 2x - 3$.

x	–2	-1	0	1	2	3	4
x^2	4					9	
$-2x$	4					-6	
-3	-3					-3	
$y=x^2-2x-3$	5					0	

b) Draw a pair of axes with the axis from –2 to 4 and the y-axis from –5 to 5.
Plot the graph $y = x^2 - 2x - 3$, joining the coordinates from the table of values, with a smooth curve. Label the curve.

c) Using your graph, solve the following quadratics:

i) $x^2 - 2x - 3 = 0$

ii) $x^2 - 2x - 3 = -3$

Questions on Solving Eq's with Graphs

As if that wasn't exciting enough, you can do the same thing with Cubic graphs...

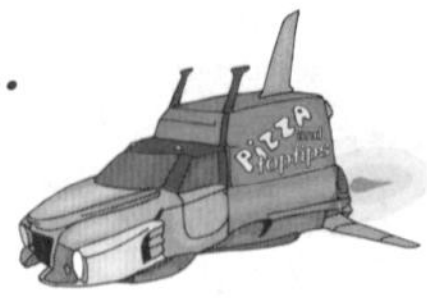

Solving Cubic Equations

1) Construct a table of values and plot the graph.
2) The graph will always be a smooth curve so you must plot several points to enable you to draw the curve accurately.
3) Use your graph to find the solution.

Q3 Solve (to 1 DP):

a) $x^3 - 3x + 4 = 4$

b) $x^3 - 3x + 4 = 2$

c) $x^3 - 3x + 4 = 6$

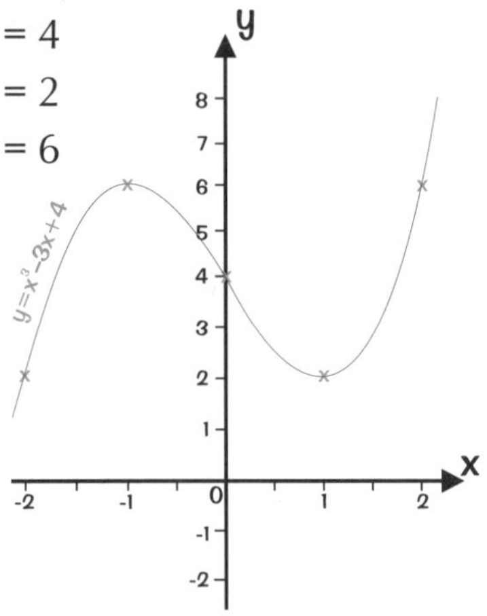

Q4 Solve (to 1 DP):

a) $2x - x^3 + 2 = 2$

b) $2x - x^3 + 2 = 6$

c) $2x - x^3 + 2 = 3$

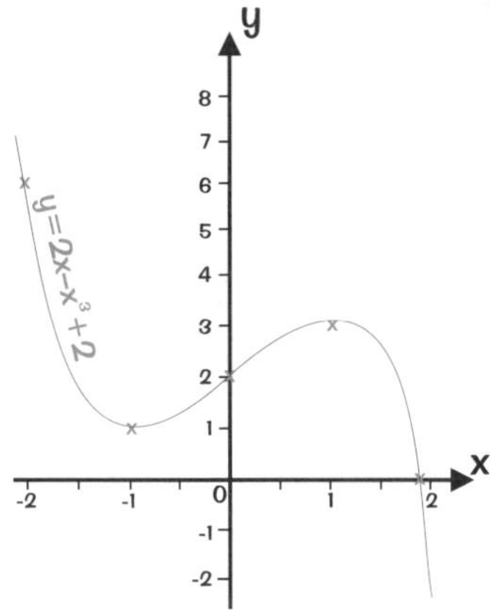

If you're asked to estimate answers to 1 dp, you need to be extra careful with the plotting. If it's not a really smooth graph, your estimates aren't going to be near enough.

Q5 Complete the table of values below for the cubic graph $y = x^3 - 2x + 1$.

x	−2	−1.5	−1	−0.5	0	0.5	1	1.5	2
x^3	−8	−3.375		−0.125					
−2x	+4	+3		+1					
+1	+1	+1		+1					
$y=x^3-2x+1$	−3			+1.9					

Approximate to 1 d.p.

Never join the coordinates with a ruler, always a curve

a) Draw a pair of axes with the x-axis from −2 to 2 (using a scale of 2 cm to 1 unit along the x-axis) and the y-axis from −3 to 6 (using a scale of 1 cm to 1 unit along the y-axis). Using the table of values plot the cubic graph $y = x^3 - 2x + 1$, joining up the points with a smooth curve. Label the graph.

b) Draw the straight line y = -1 and use it to find the solution to the equation $x^3 - 2x + 1 = -1$, giving your answer to 1 DP.

c) Draw the straight line y = 1 and use it to find the three solutions to the equation $x^3 - 2x + 1 = 1$, giving your answers to 1 DP.

What you want to do here is draw as big a graph as you can — it'll be easier to read off the answers, especially when you have to make them accurate to one decimal place.

Questions on Inequalities

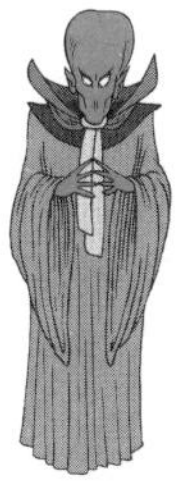

Yet another one of those bits of Maths that looks worse than it is — these are just like equations, really, except for the symbols.

The 4 Inequality Symbols:	
> means greater than	< means less than
⩾ means greater than or equal to	⩽ means less than or equal to

Inequalities can be represented on number lines. You need to know this notation, too:

Eg 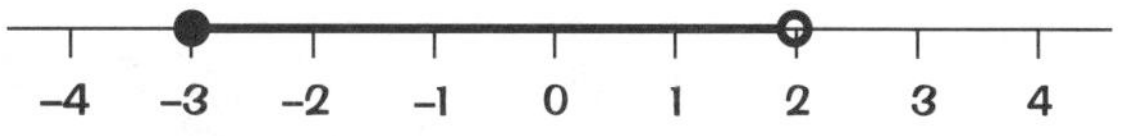

represents the inequality $-3 \leqslant x < 2$

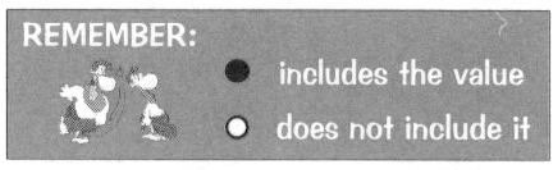

Q1 Write down an inequality for each of the diagrams below.

a) 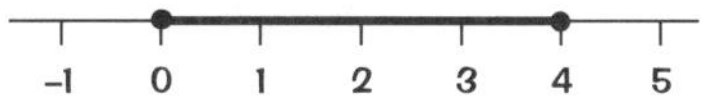

b) 

c) 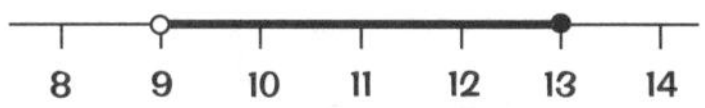

d) 

e) 

f) 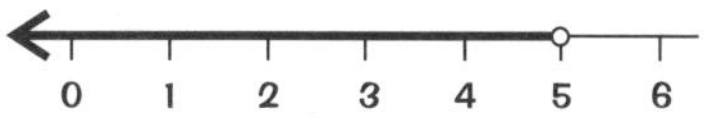

Don't forget that $(-x)^2 = x^2$, so $\sqrt{x^2} = x$ <u>or</u> $-x$.
Now, when you get an x^2 in inequality questions, the answer is anywhere between those two square roots or anywhere either side of them (depending on the inequality sign) — so you get a range of values for x

e.g. $x^2 < 4$ means $-2 < x < 2$

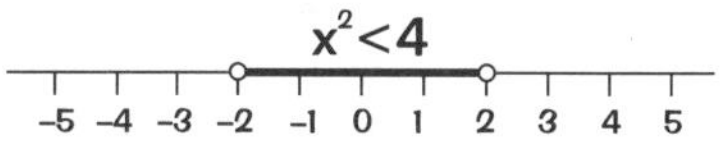

Q2 For each of the following, draw and label a number line from <u>–5 to 5</u> and use it to represent the inequality:

a) $x^2 \leqslant 4$ **c)** $x^2 \leqslant 9$ **e)** $16 \geqslant x^2$ **g)** $9 > x^2$
b) $x^2 < 1$ **d)** $25 \geqslant x^2$ **f)** $x^2 \leqslant 1$ **h)** $x^2 \leqslant 0$

Whenever you MULTIPLY OR DIVIDE BY A <u>NEGATIVE NUMBER</u>, you must <u>FLIP THE INEQUALITY SIGN</u>.

Eg	$6 - 3x > 15$	1st subtract 6 from each side
	$-3x > 9$	Next ÷ by -3
	<u>$x < -3$</u>	Change the direction of the inequality sign

Q3 Solve the following inequalities:

a) $4x > -20$
b) $x + 2 > 5$
c) $5 + x \geqslant 12$
d) $x/4 > 10$
e) $x/3 \leqslant 1$
f) $x/8 > 10$
g) $3x + 12 \leqslant 30$
h) $2x - 7 \geqslant 8$
i) $-x > 2$
j) $2x/3 > 9$
k) $3x/4 > -9$
l) $3x + 2 > 11$
m) $2(5x - 4) < 32$
n) $5(x + 2) \geqslant 25$
o) $4(x - 1) > 40$
p) $4(x + 3) \leqslant 32$

Q4 There are <u>1130</u> pupils in a school and no classes have more than <u>32</u> pupils. How many <u>classrooms</u> could be used? Show this information as an inequality.

Q5 A person is prepared to spend <u>£300</u> taking friends out to celebrate. If the restaurant charges <u>£12 per head</u>, how many guests could be invited? Show this information as an inequality.

Questions on Graphical Inequalities

Inequalities can be represented quite neatly by shading areas on graphs — but it can get quite confusing when you're trying to work out which side of the line to shade. Instead of rushing in with a guess, always check with a coordinate first.

Example:

Show on a graph the region satisfying the inequality $y \leqslant 2x + 1$

Table of values for $y = 2x + 1$

x	0	1	2
y	1	3	5

To decide which side of the line to shade try (0,0)

$y \leqslant 2x + 1$

$(0) \leqslant 2x(0) + 1$

$0 \leqslant 1$ which is <u>true</u>

∴ the region with (0,0) is the region showing $y < 2x + 1$

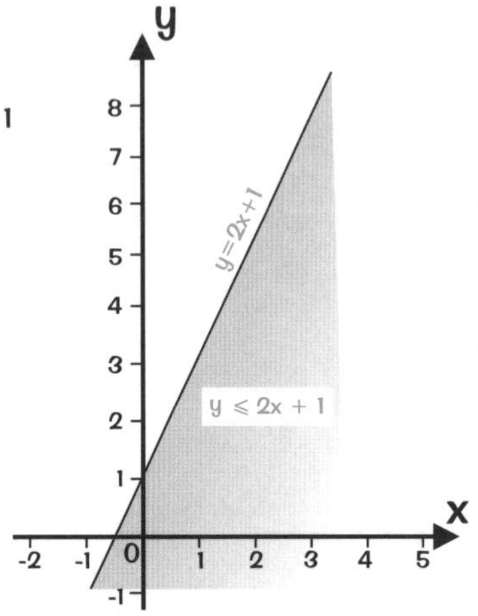

REMEMBER:

For $y \leqslant$ or $\geqslant$, the line is a solid line.
For < or >, the line is a dotted line.

The easiest coordinate to try is <u>(0,0)</u>, but you can't use it if the line goes through <u>(0,0)</u>, so try something like (1,0), (0,1) or (1,1) — it's always best to keep it simple.

Q1 Choose the correct inequality represented by the <u>shaded regions</u> on the following graphs.

a) Is the shaded region
$x + y > 4$
$x + y \geqslant 4$
$x + y < 4$ or
$x + y \leqslant 4$?

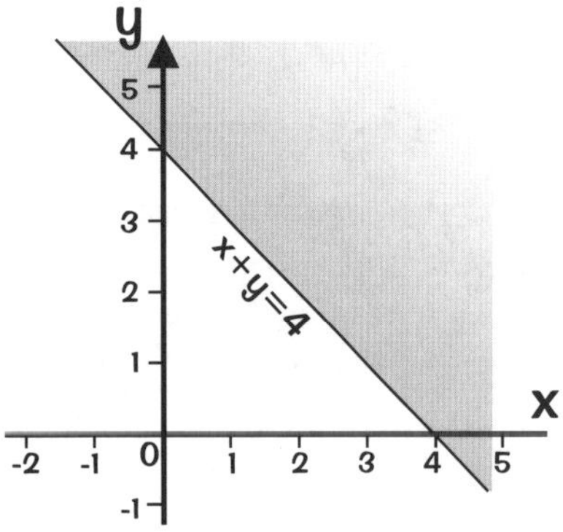

c) Is the shaded region
$y \geqslant x - 1$
$y \leqslant x - 1$
$y > x - 1$ or
$y < x - 1$?

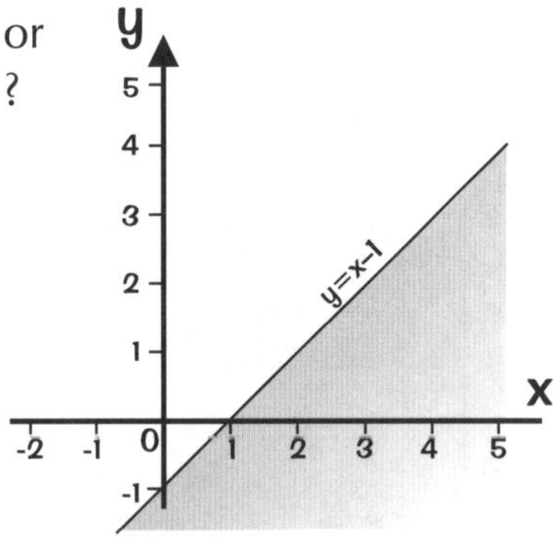

b) Is the shaded region
$x + y \geqslant 2$
$x + y \leqslant 2$
$x + y > 2$ or
$x + y < 2$?

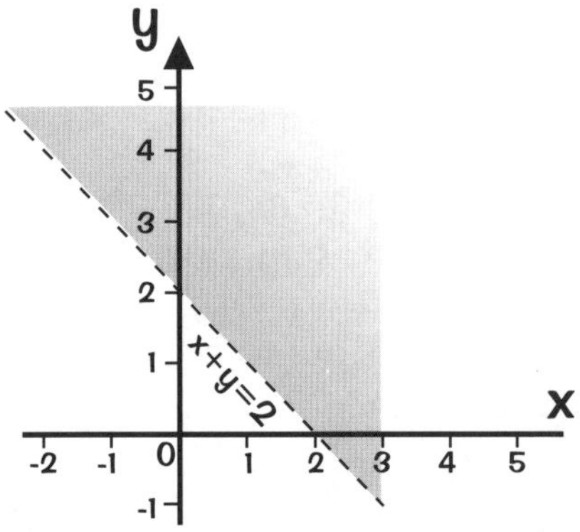

d) Is the shaded region
$3y \geqslant 3 - 2x$
$3y \leqslant 3 - 2x$
$3y > 3 - 2x$ or
$3y < 3 - 2x$?

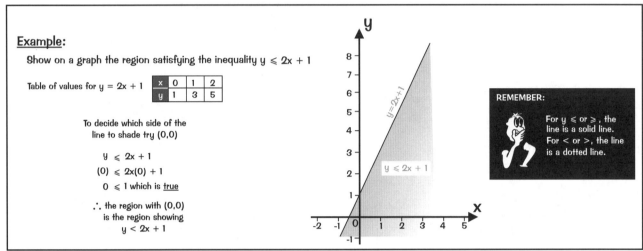

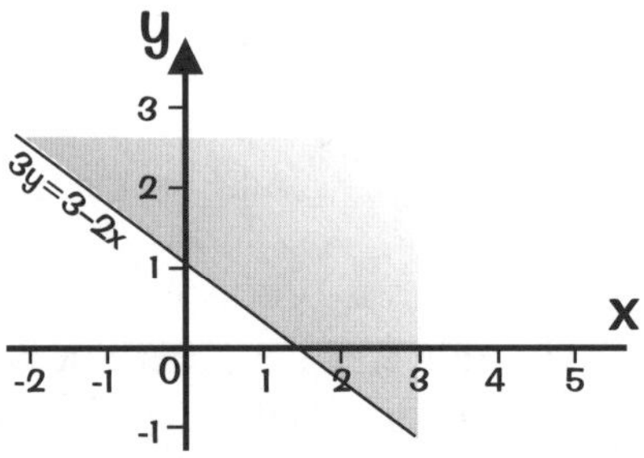

Questions on Gradients of Lines

It's easy to make a hash of this, but what you've got to remember is:
1) X comes before Y, and 2) X is a-cross (hmmm).

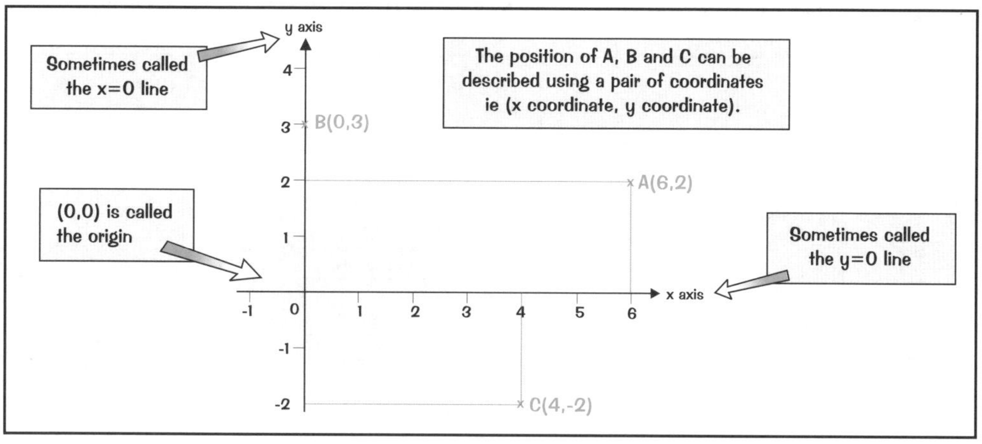

If you forget these, it'll all go completely pear-shaped.

Q1 Draw a set of axes with x from –5 to 5 and y from –5 to 5.
Using these <u>axes</u> and the two <u>tables of values</u>, draw and label the <u>two lines</u>.

a)

x	-4	-1	0	2
y	-4	-1	0	2

b)

x	-4	-2	0	3	5
y	4	2	0	-3	-5

$$\text{Gradient of line AB} = \frac{\text{y-coordinate of B} - \text{y-coordinate of A}}{\text{x-coordinate of B} - \text{x-coordinate of A}}$$

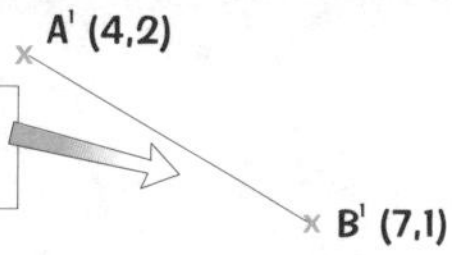

'Downhill' gradients are always <u>negative</u>

$$\text{Gradient of line A'B'} = \frac{1-2}{7-4} = -\frac{1}{3}$$

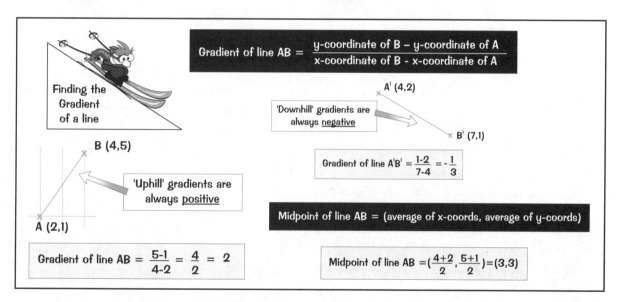

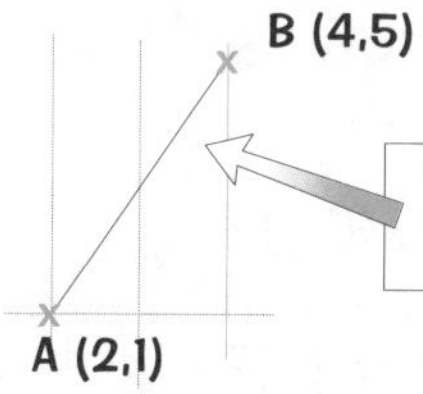

'Uphill' gradients are always <u>positive</u>

Midpoint of line AB = (average of x-coords, average of y-coords)

$$\text{Gradient of line AB} = \frac{5-1}{4-2} = \frac{4}{2} = 2$$

$$\text{Midpoint of line AB} = \left(\frac{4+2}{2}, \frac{5+1}{2}\right) = (3,3)$$

Q2 Draw axes with x from -9 to 9 and y from -12 to 12. On this set of axes join each <u>pair of points</u> and work out the <u>gradient</u> and the <u>midpoint</u> of the line.

A is (1, 1), B is (2, 4), gradient of AB = ?
C is (2, 7), D is (6, 9), gradient of CD = ?
E is (5, 5), F is (7, 0), gradient of EF = ?
G is (-7, 7), H is (-2, 10), gradient of GH =?

Q3 Using axes with x from -4 to 4 and y from -4 to 4, draw the following <u>three graphs</u>:

a)

x	-2	-1	0	1	2
y	-4	-2	0	2	4

b)

x	-4	-2	0	2	4
y	-2	-1	0	1	2

c)

x	-1	0	1
y	3	0	-3

Questions on Recognising Graphs

Remember, you're going to need to be able to sketch a graph from memory — scary, huh. Don't worry — they don't expect you to remember them all (phew) but here are the ones you really need to know:

1) Straight line graph: $y = mx+c$

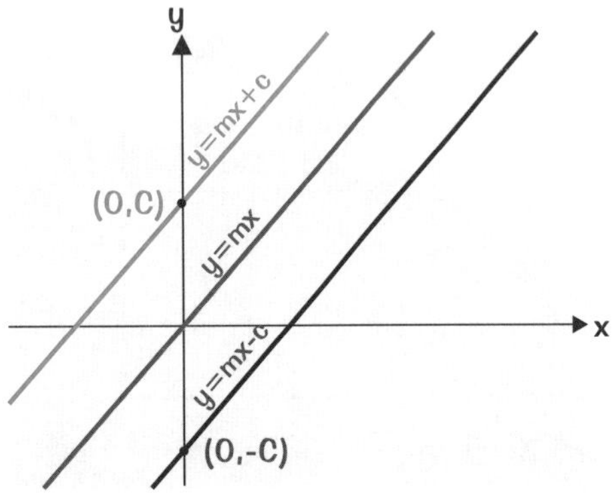

2) Reciprocal graphs: $y = a/x$

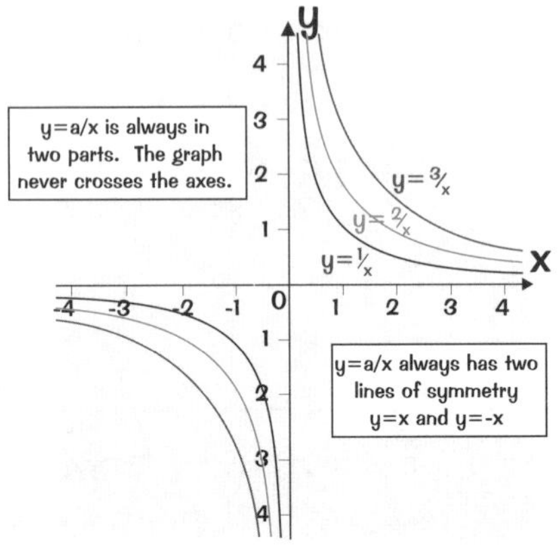

3) Quadratic graphs: $y = ax^2$

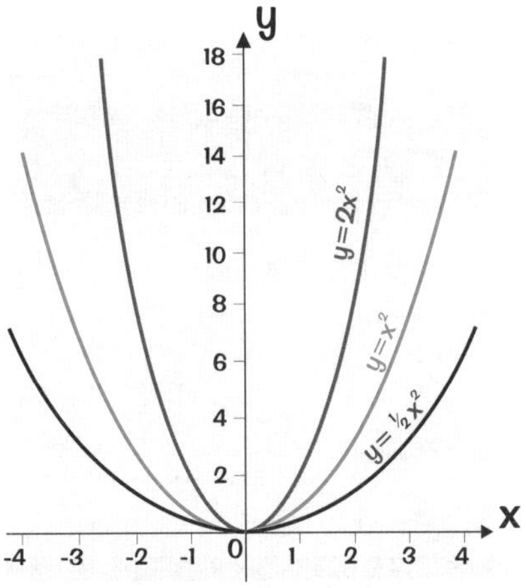

You can't find the reciprocal of zero because you can't divide by zero. So the reciprocal graph always has two parts — in diagonally opposite quadrants from each other — and neither touches the origin.

Q1 Sketch the graph of $y = 4/x$ for values of x between -4 and 4, by first completing the table of values.

x	-4	-3	-2	-1	0	1	2	3	4
y			-2		✕			$1\frac{1}{3}$	

Q2 Sketch the following graphs:

a) $y = 5/x$
b) $y = x + 5$
c) $y = 5 - x$
d) $y = x^2 + 2$
e) $y = x^2 + 2x$
f) $y = x^2 + x + 1$
g) $y = 4x^2$
h) $y = 3x^2 - 1$
i) $y = 2x^2 + x - 6$
j) $y = 2x^2 + x$
k) $y = x + x^2$
l) $y = 7/x$
m) $y = 6x - 2$
n) $y = x - x^2$
o) $y = -x^2$
p) $y = -1/x$

Anyway, if you get stuck, you can always plot a graph using a table of values.

Questions on Straight Line Graphs

The very first thing you've got to do is work out a table of values.

Example: Draw the graph of $y = 3x - 1$ for values of x between 0 and 4.

1) First complete a table of values:

x	0	1	2	3	4
y	-1	2	5	8	11

decided by the question (x row)

worked out using $y = 3x - 1$ (y row)

2) Draw the axes.
3) Plot the points.
4) Label the line $y = 3x - 1$.
(step 4 has been left for you to complete)

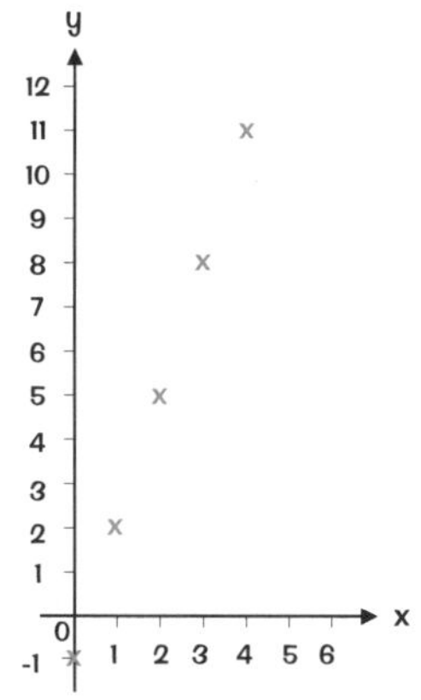

Q1 **a)** Complete the table below, for $y = x + 2$.

x	0	1	2	3	4	5	6
y	2			5			

b) Use your table of values to draw the graph $y = x + 2$.

c) Where does your graph cross the y-axis?

d) What is the gradient of your graph?

Q2 By drawing the graph of $y = 3x - 3$, find where it crosses the y-axis and the gradient.

Q3 Find the y-intercept (where it crosses the y-axis) and the gradient of the graph $y = \frac{1}{2}x + 3$.

Every straight line graph can be written in the form:—

$$y = mx + c$$

The number multiplying the x term tells you the gradient of the graph (m)

The number by itself tells you where the graph crosses the y axis. This is the y-intercept (c)

Q4 The following are equations of linear graphs. Without plotting the graphs, state the gradient of each graph and the y-intercept.

a) $y = 4x + 2$
b) $y = 5x - 1$
c) $y = 6x$
d) $y = 5 + 2x$
e) $y = 12 - 3x$
f) $y = x$
g) $y = 3 - x$
h) $y + 2x = 10$
i) $2y = x + 4$
j) $y + 5 = 4x$

Q5 Find the gradient of each of these lines, and state the y-intercept. Hence find the equations for each of these linear graphs.

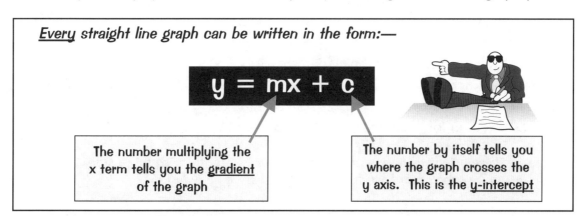

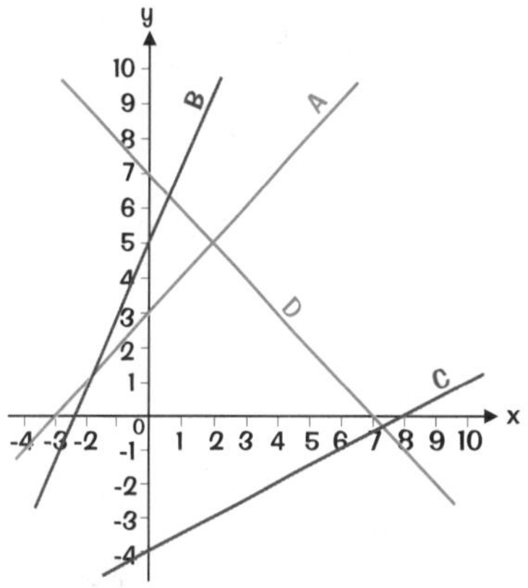

Q6 Draw axes with x from 0 to 5 and y from 0 to 4. Draw the straight line which passes through (1, 2) and (5, 4).
Find the gradient of the line and the y-intercept.
State the equation of the graph.

Questions on Travel Graphs

Travel graphs are also called <u>distance-time graphs</u>, because they always show the distance (along the y-axis) against time (along the x-axis).

Q1 The travel graph shows the <u>journey</u> of a girl cycling from home to her grandparents' house and returning.

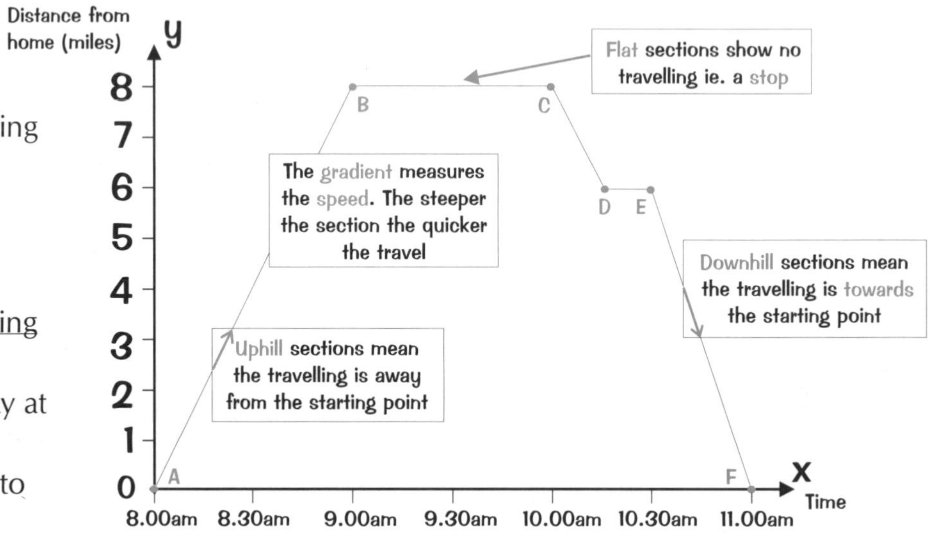

a) Which <u>section</u> of the graph shows her cycling <u>to</u> her grandparents? (Use the letters to describe it.)

b) Which section of the graph shows her <u>visiting</u> her grandparents?

c) How <u>long</u> did she stay at her grandparents?

d) How <u>long</u> did it take to cycle <u>there</u>?

e) How <u>far away</u> do her grandparents live?

f) How <u>fast</u> was she travelling when she cycled <u>to</u> her grandparents?

g) What <u>time</u> did she set off to <u>return</u> home?

h) How <u>far</u> did she travel <u>towards</u> home before she had to <u>stop</u>?

i) How <u>long</u> did she stop for?

j) How <u>far away</u> from home was she when she stopped?

k) If she <u>started</u> cycling again at E, at what <u>speed</u> did she travel for this final leg of her journey?

l) What time did she <u>arrive home</u>?

m) Suggest a <u>reason</u> for the graph being flat between <u>D and E</u>.

These questions have always got loads of bits to them, so make sure you're happy with how the graphs work before you start.

Q2 The travel graph shows the journey of a boy going on a run.

a) Between what times was the boy running the <u>fastest</u>?

b) Calculate his <u>fastest speed</u> in km/hr.

c) For how long was the boy <u>resting</u>?

d) What happened to the boy's speed at <u>B</u>?

e) What was the boy's speed for the <u>first 15 mins</u> of his run?

f) What was the boy's speed for the <u>next 15 mins</u> of his run?

g) How <u>far</u> did the boy run?

h) What was the <u>average speed</u> for his entire run?

i) Suggest a <u>reason</u> for the boy being able to <u>return</u> home <u>quicker</u> than when he started his run.

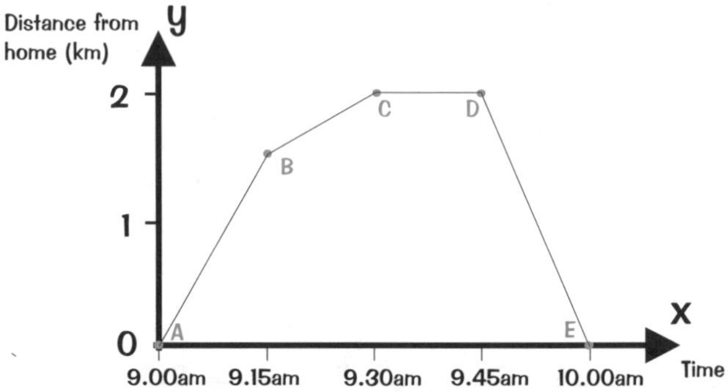

Remember:

$$\text{Average speed} = \frac{\text{total dist. travelled}}{\text{total time taken}}$$

Questions on Real Life Graphs

Conversion graphs let you swap from one unit to another, just by reading the graph — what fun.

Q1 Using the conversion graph convert the following to km, rounding your answers to the nearest km:

a) 5 miles → km **c)** 10 miles → km

b) 20 miles → km **d)** 27 miles → km

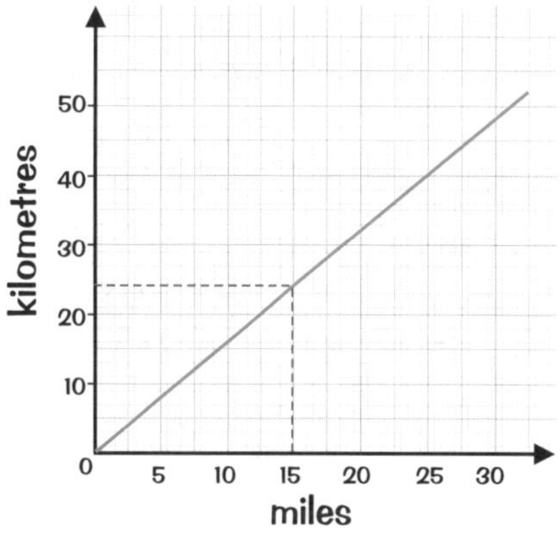

Q2 Find the gradient of the graph.

Careful — the axes have different scales. (One square is 5 miles, but 10 kilometres)

Sometimes they'll only want the shape of a graph, so you can just sketch it. A sketch graph doesn't have any points plotted, but you still need to draw a pair of labelled axes (with a ruler, of course).

Q3 Show the general relationship between these quantities by sketching a graph for each case. Place the first quantity mentioned on the y-axis.

a) The level of water in a rectangular tank when drained at a constant rate, against time.

b) The volumes of cubes with edges of different lengths.

c) The amount raised per mile on a sponsored walk.

d) The area of an equilateral triangle compared to the length of an edge.

When you're doing these questions, ask yourself these three main things:—

1) is it a straight line or a curved one?

2) will the line be horizontal, vertical, uphill or downhill?

3) will it cross either of the axes and if it does, will it be left, right, above or below the origin?

Q4 Water is poured into each of these containers at a constant rate.

Match the containers to the graphs showing the depth of water (d) against time (t) taken to fill the container.

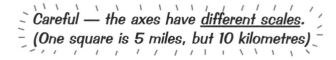

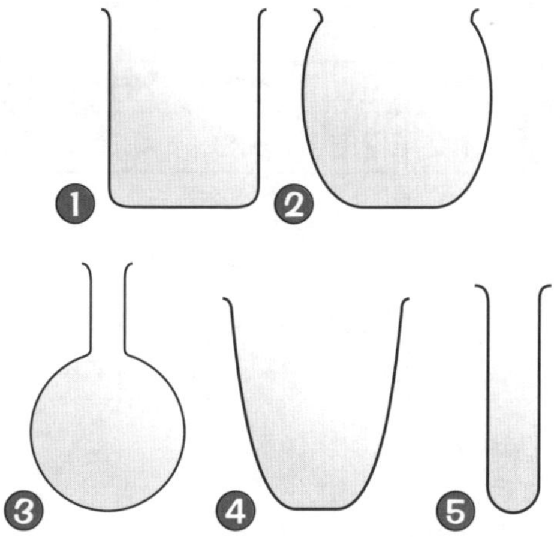

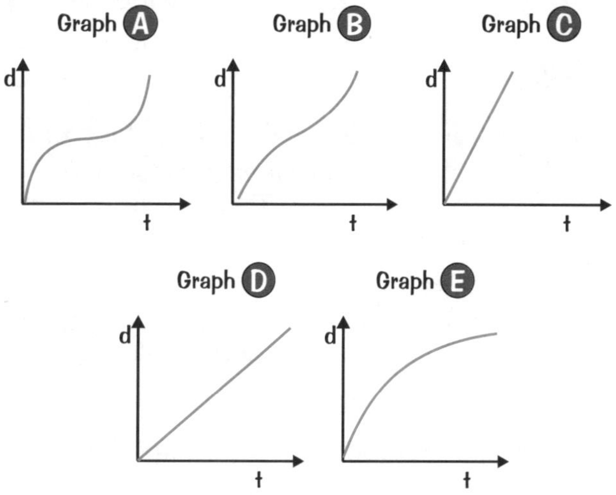

Questions on Real Life Graphs

This is the same sort of thing — drawing graphs from bits of real life information. How exciting.

Q5 A telephone company charges £21 per quarter to rent a line and 5p per unit used.
Plot a graph showing the number of units used along the x-axis, with x from 0 to 800 units and the cost in £ per quarter, of the corresponding telephone bill, along the y-axis.

a) A household uses 600 units per quarter. Use your graph to predict their bill.

b) A household can opt to join a new scheme. The new billing system will only benefit the household if their quarterly bill is £50 or more.
How many units would this mean using per quarter before the new scheme would be of benefit to them?

c) A household receives a quarterly bill for £35.50. Estimate the number of units used that quarter.

Q6 Three plumbers, A, B and C, charge at different rates for their work.

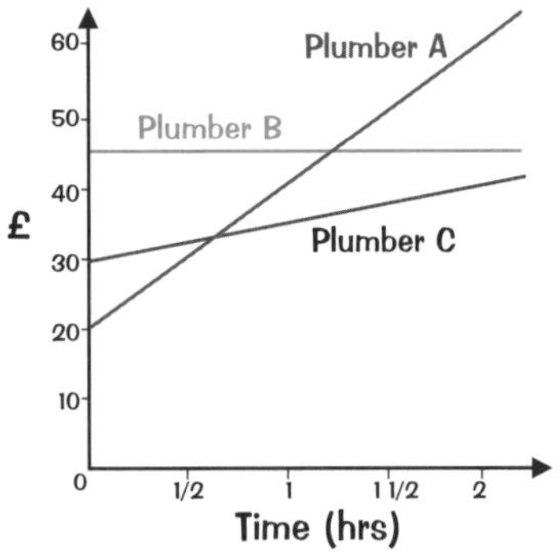

The three lines on the graph show the relationship between time taken and their bill. Use the graphs to describe how each plumber charges their customers.

a) If a burst pipe takes 30 minutes to fix, which is the cheapest plumber to call and what is their bill likely to be?

b) If a washing machine takes $1\frac{3}{4}$ hrs to install, which is the cheapest plumber to call, and what is their bill likely to be?

This sort of question seems to be a favourite for exam papers — which is why you've had 3 pages of questions to warm up to it.

Q7 The cost for hiring a car is £20 plus an additional charge of 20p per mile.
Draw a graph to show the cost of hiring the car for any mileage, up to 100 miles.

a) Use your graph to determine the cost of a journey covering 48 miles.

b) A holidaymaker has a budget of £40. What is the maximum journey length the holidaymaker can afford to make?

Q8 A piece of wire gave the following values of resistance, R (ohms), at various voltage readings, V (volts). These experimental results are thought to follow the rule $R = mV + c$, where m and c are constants.

V	10	20	30	40	50
R	9.2	7.6	5.9	4.5	3.1

By plotting V along the x-axis and R along the y-axis, check whether the results lie approximately in a straight line. If so, find estimates for the values of m and c.

Q9 As a kettle boiled its temperature was recorded.

Time (mins)	0	1/2	1	1 1/2	2	2 1/2	3
Temp (°C)	19	21	24	29	40	59	100

Plot the points and join them up with a smooth curve.

a) Estimate how long it took to heat up the water to 50°C.

b) Estimate how long it took to heat up the water from 50°C to 100°C.

Questions on Transformations

You've got to be able to give all the details for each type — and it will be in the Exam.

Use the word TERRY to remember the 4 transformations:	***Always specifiy ALL the details:***
T ranslation	1) VECTOR OF TRANSLATION
E nlargement	1) SCALE FACTOR 2) CENTRE OF ENLARGEMENT
R eflection	1) MIRROR LINE
R otation	1) ANGLE TURNED 2) DIRECTION 3) CENTRE OF ROTATION
Y	

The Y doesn't stand for anything, in case you're wondering...

Q1 Write down the translation vectors for the translations shown.

a)

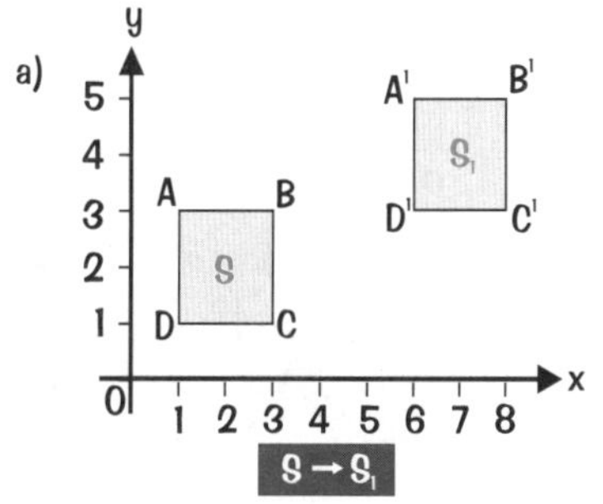

b)

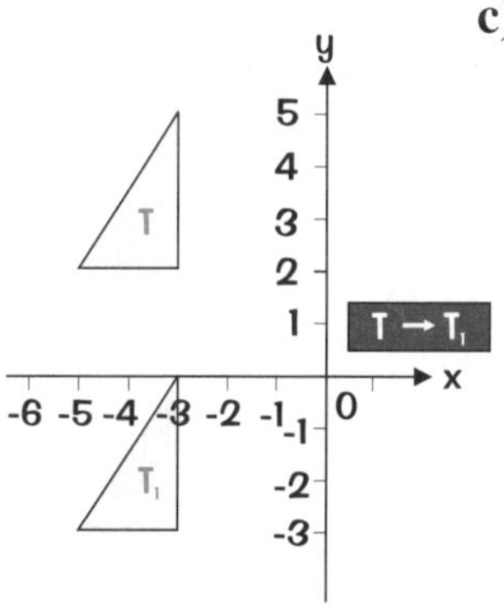

c)

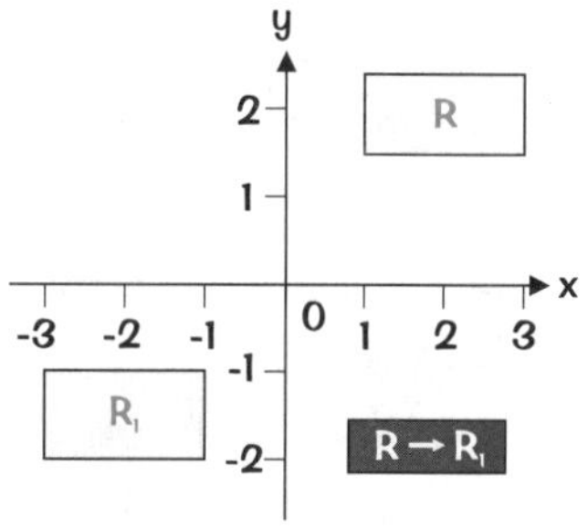

Q2

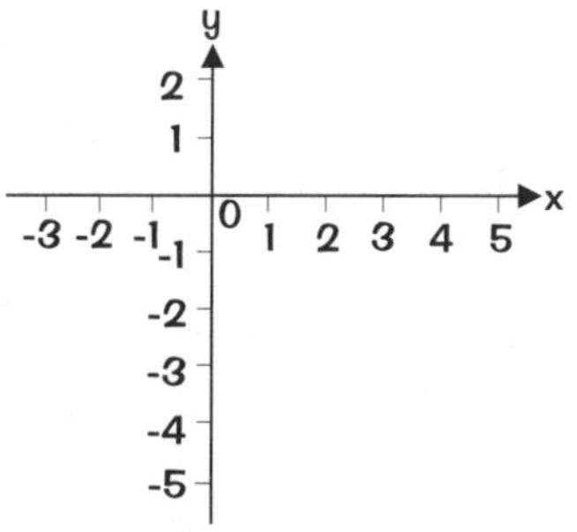

Copy this set of axes and plot D (3,-2).
Now translate the point D, and draw the image of point D after translation under each of the vectors:

a) $\begin{pmatrix}1\\2\end{pmatrix}$, Label D_1

b) $\begin{pmatrix}-3\\-2\end{pmatrix}$, Label D_2

c) $\begin{pmatrix}1\\-1\end{pmatrix}$, Label D_3

d) $\begin{pmatrix}-4\\0\end{pmatrix}$, Label D_4

Q3 A translation maps (4, 2) onto (7, 4). What is the image point of (-1, 6) under the identical translation?

Q4 A translation maps the point P(2, 1) onto P_1(1, 2). P_1 is then mapped onto P_2 via the translation $\begin{pmatrix}-4\\2\end{pmatrix}$. By coordinate axes or otherwise decide:

a) What is the translation that maps P onto P_1?

b) Where is the point P_2?

c) What single translation would map P onto P_2, directly?

d) What single translation would map P_2 back to P, directly?

Questions on Transformations

There are only 4 transformations — Translation, Enlargement, Rotation and Reflection. Make sure you know them all — and I mean really know them — so you can spot them in combinations.

Q5 Draw the result of reflecting this shape in

a) the x-axis

b) the y-axis.

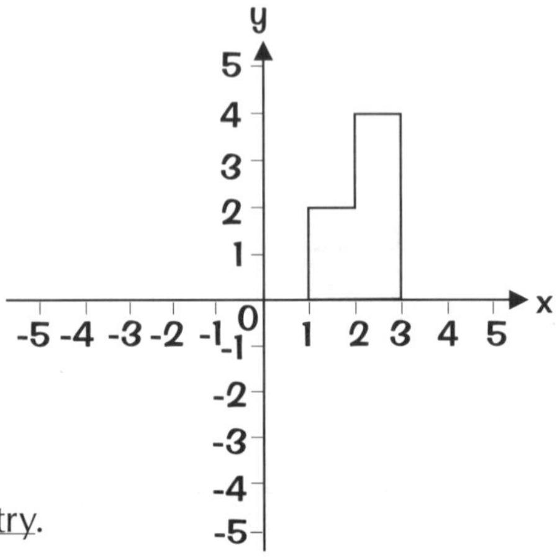

Q6 Plot each of the following points on graph paper. Join them together with straight lines in alphabetical order to form a closed shape.

A(0, 0) B(0, 2) C(2, 4)
D(4, 2) E(2, 2) F(2, 0)

a) Reflect the shape in the y-axis.

b) Reflect the original shape in the x-axis.

c) Complete the drawing so that it has 2 lines of symmetry.

Q7 PQRS is a parallelogram where P is the point (-1, 3), Q is the point (-2, 1½), R is the point (?, ?) and S is the point (-3, 3).

a) What are the coordinates of the point R?

b) Plot the parallelogram on squared paper.

c) Draw in the line y = x, on the same diagram.

d) Reflect PQRS in the line y = x.

e) Under this transformation, what are the coordinates of the reflected points P′, Q′, R′ and S′?

f) Write a sentence, or show by example, what happens to the x and y coordinates when reflected in the line y = x.

Q8

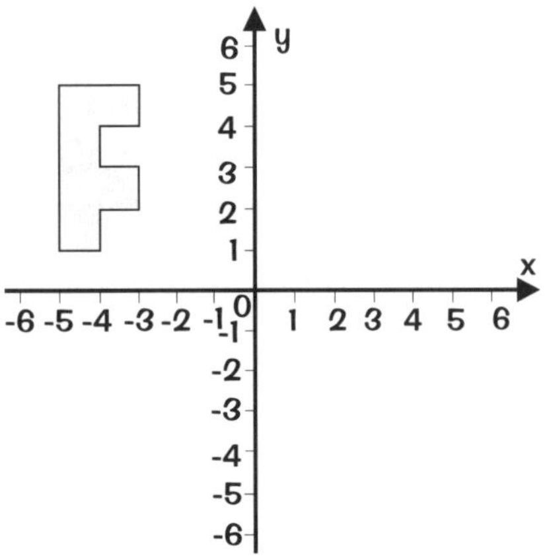

a) Draw the image of F after a rotation through 90° anti-clockwise about (0, 0).

b) Start again with the original F and rotate it through 180° about (0, 0). Call the image F_2.

c) How would you transform F_2 back to the original F?

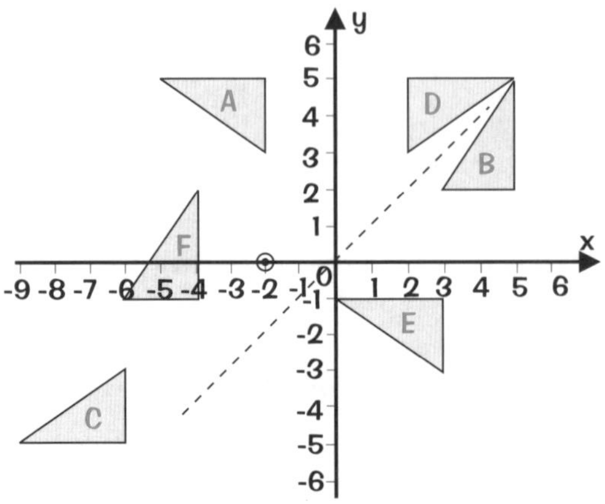

Q9 Look at the graph to the right and describe fully the transformations which place:

a) A onto E

b) A onto D

c) D onto B

d) D onto C

e) B onto F

f) F onto B

Q10 Start with the points A (1, 0), B (3, 3), C (3, 0) which define a triangle. By using graph paper or otherwise, redefine the new points under the transformation 'enlargement scale factor 2 centre (6, 0)' followed by a rotation, centre (0, 0), of 90° anti-clockwise.

Questions on Transformations

Δ ABC means "the triangle with vertices A, B and C". And you'd never have worked that one out if I hadn't told you...

Q11 In the diagram Δ K″L″M″ is the image of Δ KLM after it has been rotated about (0,0) 90° anti-clockwise and then translated by $\begin{pmatrix}-3\\-1\end{pmatrix}$.

By using inverse transformations,

a) Find Δ K'L'M' after the inverse translation has been applied to Δ K″L″M″. Draw it on the diagram.

b) Find Δ KLM (the original triangle) after applying the inverse rotation to Δ K'L'M'. Draw it on the diagram.

c) Check by doing the complete joint transformation on Δ KLM to see that you end up at Δ K″L″M″.

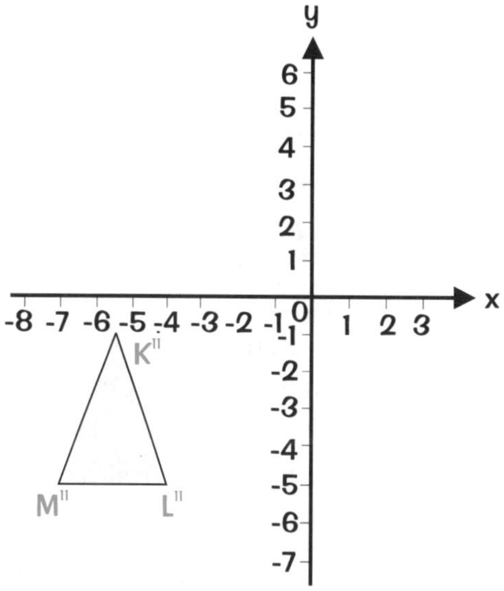

Q12 The points L(3, 1), M(5, 4), N(8, 4), P(8, 1) define a trapezium LMNP.

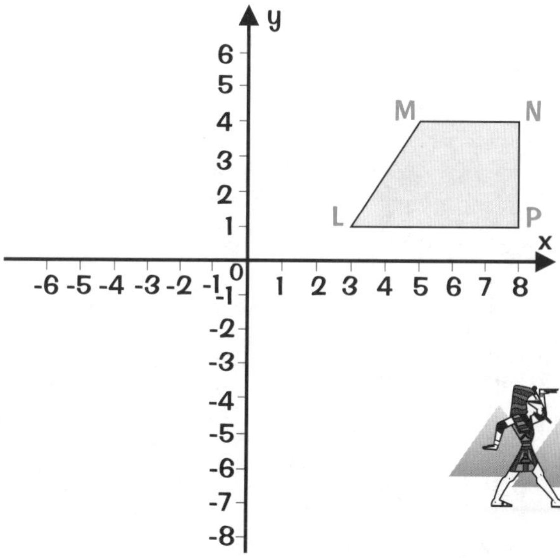

L' (-1,-5), M' (-3,-8), N'(-6,-8), P'(-6,-5) define the image of the original trapezium under a rotation through 180° about C(x,y).
By plotting L'M'N'P' on the diagram opposite, determine the point C and state the values of x and y.

There are a few vectors sneaking in here as well — urghh. Make sure you get the coordinates the right way round — top for x direction, bottom for y direction.

Q13 a) Determine the centre of enlargement and scale factor that maps PRQ onto P′ R′ Q′.

b) Are triangles PRQ and P′ R′ Q′ similar or congruent?

(See P.86 of The Revision Guide)

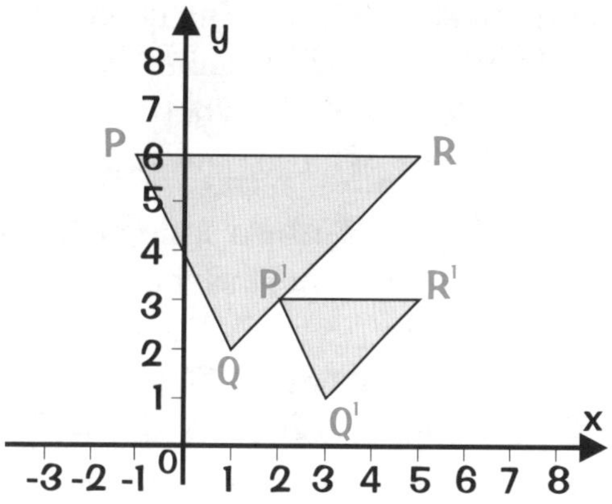

Questions on Similarity and Enlargement

You must remember the important difference between similarity and congruence.

Similarity and Congruence

See P.86 of The Revision Guide

1) Two shapes are similar if they're the same shape but different size. The lengths of the two shapes are related to the scale factor by this very important formula triangle:
2) Two shapes are congruent if they're the same size and same shape

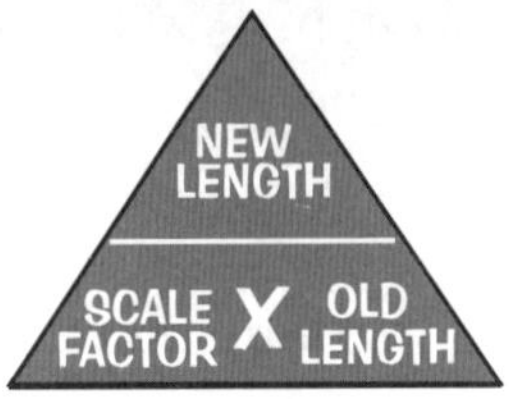

Q1 Two picture frames are shown. One picture is similar to the other. Calculate L cm, the length of the smaller frame.

Q2 For each of the following pairs:
Decide if the shapes are similar or not.
Give a reason for your answer.

a)

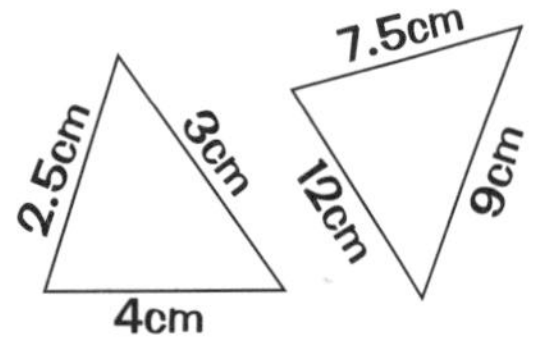

b)

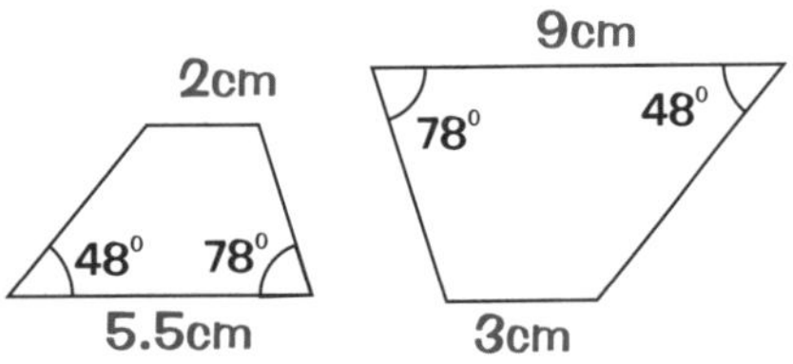

c)

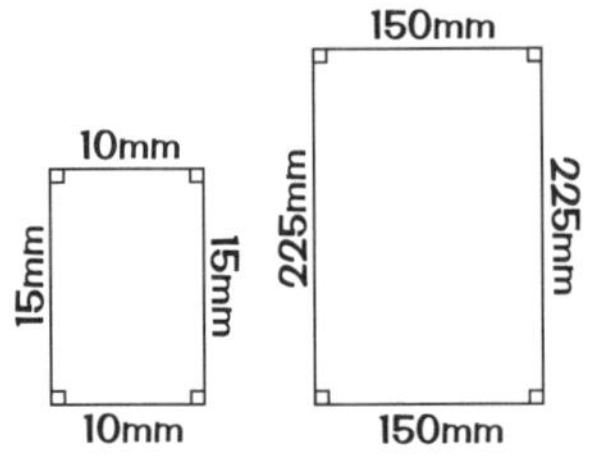

d)

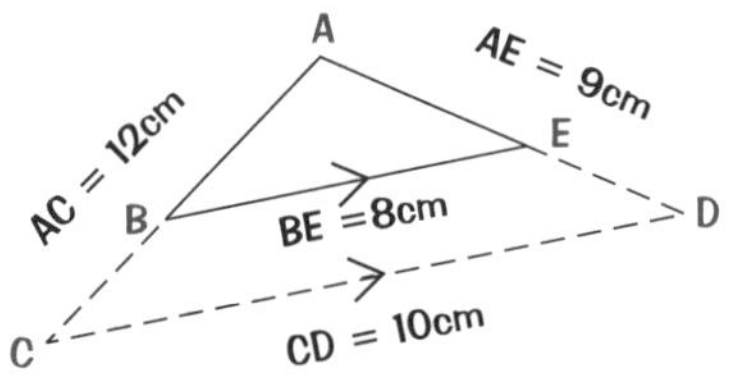

Q3 Enlarge square S by a scale factor of 4, using the ray technique or other method. The centre of enlargement is (2, 12). Label the new square K′ L′ M′ N′. What are the coordinates of these new points?

Q4 Enlarge rectangle Z by a scale factor of 3 using any method. The centre of enlargement is (2,0). Label the new rectangle W′X′Y′V′. What are the coordinates of these new points?

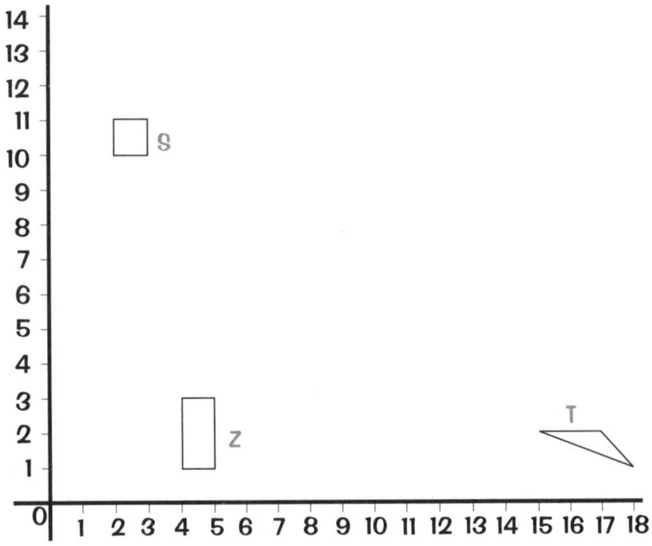

Q5 Enlarge triangle T by a scale factor of 2 about (18,0). Label this triangle T′. Reduce T′ by a scale factor of ½ about a centre of enlargement (12,0). Label this triangle T″.

a) Give the three coordinates of T″.

b) What single transformation would map T onto T″?

c) What single transformation would map T″ back onto T?

Questions on Symmetry

They do say that bad things happen in threes... and now you've got to learn three types of symmetry — but don't worry, I reckon their names pretty much give the game away.

There are THREE types of symmetry:	
1) LINE SYMMETRY	You can draw a mirror line across the object and both sides will fold together exactly.
2) PLANE SYMMETRY	This applies to 3-D solids. You can draw a plane mirror surface through the solid to make the shape exactly the same on both sides of the plane.
3) ROTATIONAL SYMMETRY	You can rotate the shape or drawing into different positions that all look exactly the same.

These questions are a piece of cake if you use tracing paper — and remember you can use it in the Exam, so take some with you or ask for it.

Q1 Mark in the lines of symmetry of the following letters. State the order of rotational symmetry for each one.

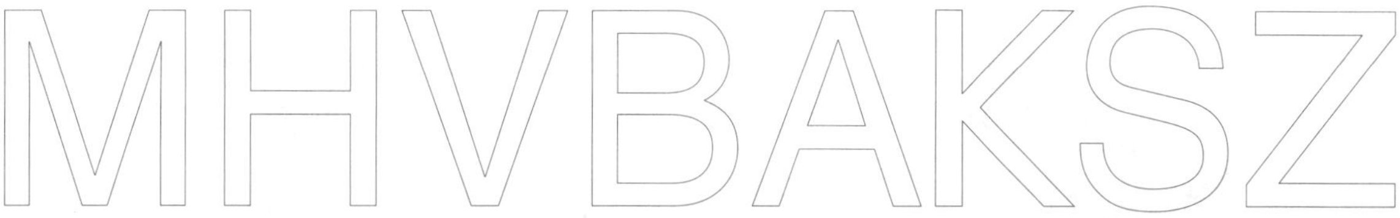

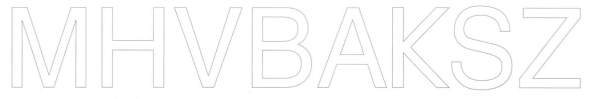

Q2 Draw an example of each of the following shapes. Put in the axes of symmetry and state the order of rotational symmetry.

a) An equilateral triangle.
b) An isosceles triangle.
c) A rhombus.
d) An isosceles trapezium.
e) A regular octagon.
f) A parallelogram.

Q3 On each cube draw in a different plane of symmetry.

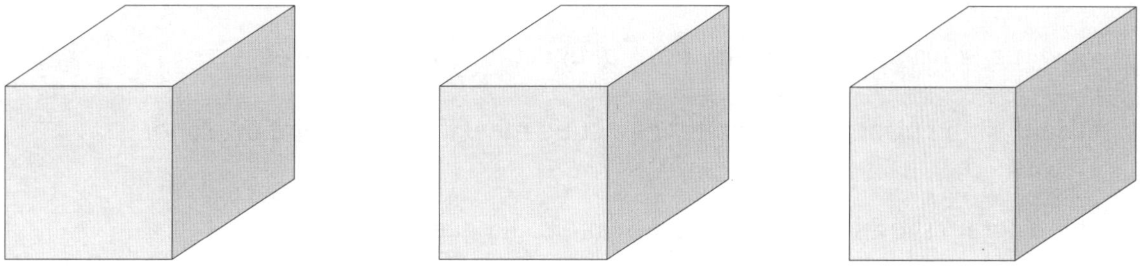

Q4 Here is a cuboid:

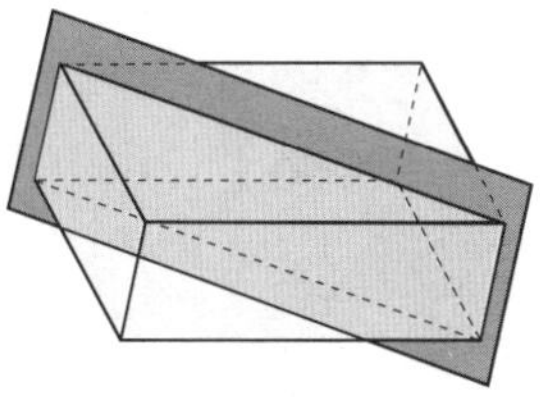

Is the plane a plane of symmetry?

Questions on Symmetry

Watch out for those 3-D solids and planes of symmetry — they're pretty hard to draw, so make sure you do this page in pencil — and have a rubber ready...

Q5 How many planes of symmetry does this <u>triangular prism</u> have?

Q6 How many planes of symmetry does a <u>circular cone</u> have?

Q7 In the square-based pyramid shown, is this a plane of symmetry?

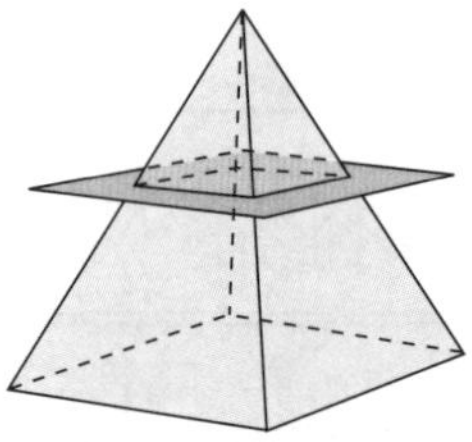

Q8 Draw in another plane of symmetry which is <u>perpendicular</u> to the one drawn in the diagram.

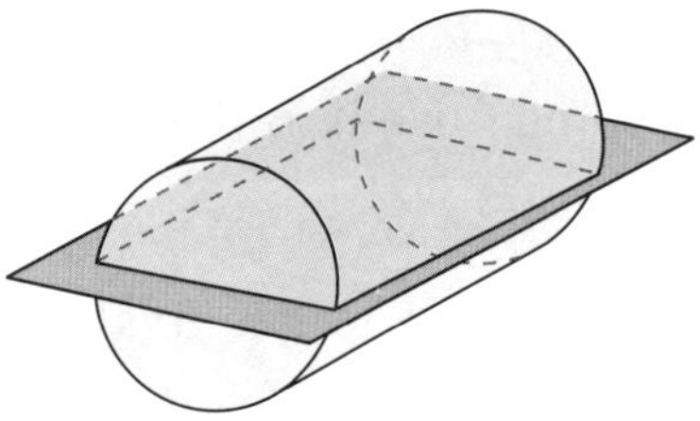

Q9

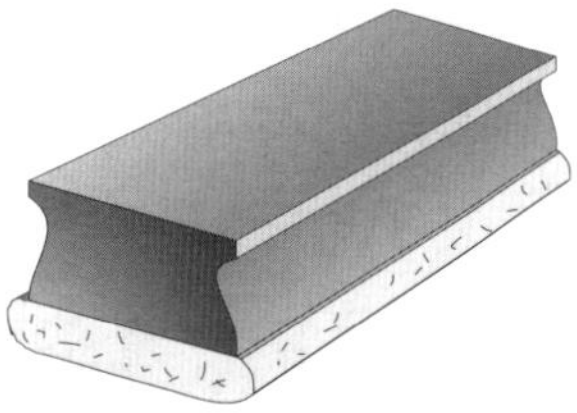

How many <u>planes of symmetry</u> does a blackboard rubber like the one shown have?

And don't think they won't try this in the Exam...

Q10 A roofing tile is shown.

a) How many planes of symmetry does this have?

b) What <u>angle</u> do they meet at?

c) <u>How</u> do they meet — in a line, point or plane?

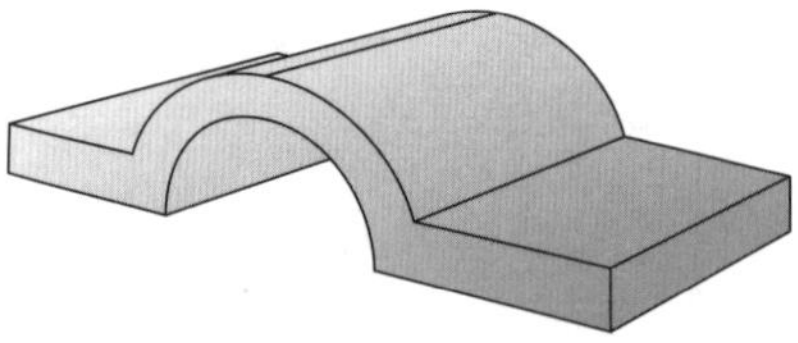

Q11 How many planes of symmetry does a regular <u>tetrahedron</u> have?

Q12 Would all the planes of symmetry of a cube meet in a <u>line</u>, <u>point</u> or <u>plane</u>?

Q13 The diagram shows a <u>square-based pyramid</u> of height X with a square base of side 2X. P is the centre of the base, whilst T is the mid-point of AB, and S is the midpoint of CD.

a) How many planes of symmetry does the square-based pyramid have?

b) Is it true that $\angle TVS$ is a <u>right angle</u>?

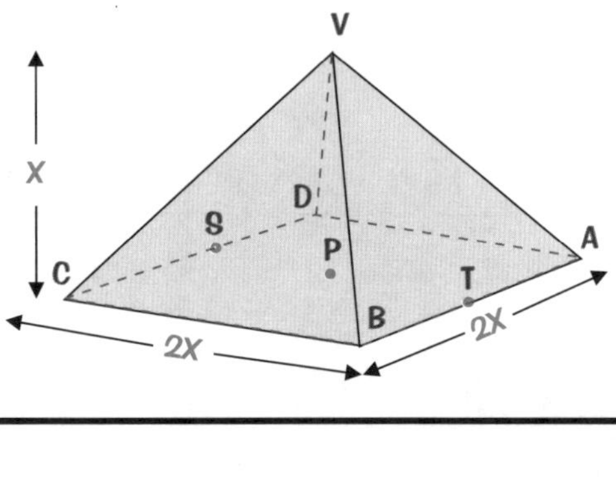

Questions on Shapes You Need To Know

You need to know about <u>all</u> of the following shapes <u>and</u> their symmetries.

Eeeek.

2-D Shapes	3-D Solids
1) SQUARE	1) REGULAR TETRAHEDRON
2) RECTANGLE	2) CYLINDER
3) RHOMBUS	3) CUBE
4) PARALLELOGRAM	4) CUBOID
5) TRAPEZIUM	5) SPHERE
6) KITE	6) TRIANGULAR PRISM
7) EQUILATERAL TRIANGLE	7) CONE
8) RIGHT-ANGLED TRIANGLE	8) SQUARE-BASED PYRAMID
9) ISOSCELES TRIANGLE	

Q1 Solve these simple riddles to find the names of 6 common shapes:

a) I have 4 sides of the same length but my two pairs of <u>parallel</u> sides are not at right angles to each other, although my <u>diagonals</u> bisect each other at 90°.

b) I am a shape that likes to fly. My two <u>isosceles</u> triangles form the four-sided shape, but if I am split down my line of symmetry I will show two <u>congruent</u> triangles instead.

c) I have four sides, 2 pairs of parallel sides, each pair of equal length but different from the other pair. I have no line of symmetry because of this and the fact that my sides don't meet at 90°.

d) I am related to a square — but I am not one.
I am related to a parallelogram — but I am not one.
I have two symmetries of <u>order 2</u>.

e) I can be one of three.
I can look like the roof of a house with a line of symmetry.
I can be one even if you join my pair of parallel sides, by any old straight lines.

f) My order of rotational symmetry = My number of lines of symmetry = My number of sides = My number of right angles.

Q2 Name 4 different triangles and draw a sketch for each one, showing appropriate, relevant differences.

Q3 Name each of the following solids. Draw in a single <u>plane</u> of symmetry if any exist:

a)

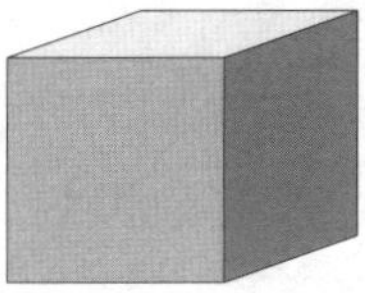

b)

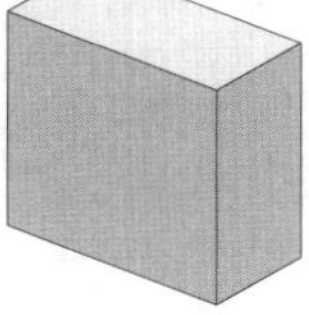

c)

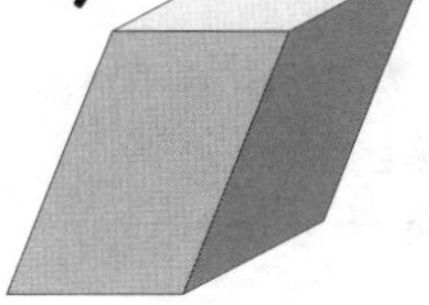

d)

e)

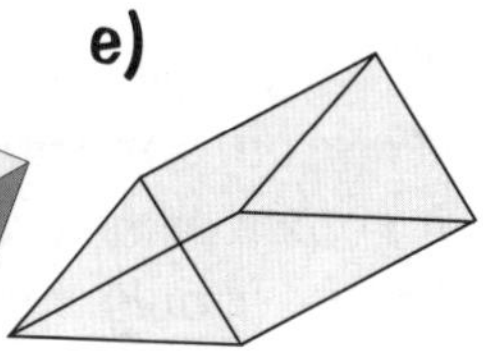

f)

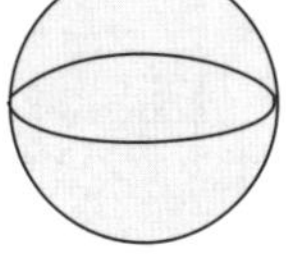

g)

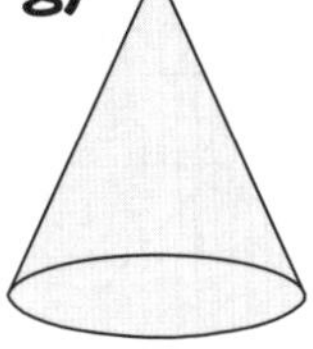

h)

i)

j)

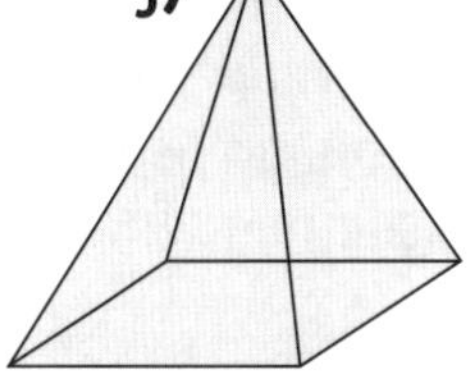

Questions on Areas

Here are the <u>Top 5 Formulas</u> — if you <u>know these</u> you can work out just about <u>any area</u>.

1) <u>Rectangle</u> $A = l \times w$

4) <u>Trapezium</u> $A = \frac{1}{2} \times (a+b) \times h$

2) <u>Triangle</u> $A = \frac{1}{2} \times b \times h_v$

5) <u>Circle</u> $A = \pi \times r^2$

3) <u>Parallelogram</u> $A = b \times h_v$ $C = \pi \times D$

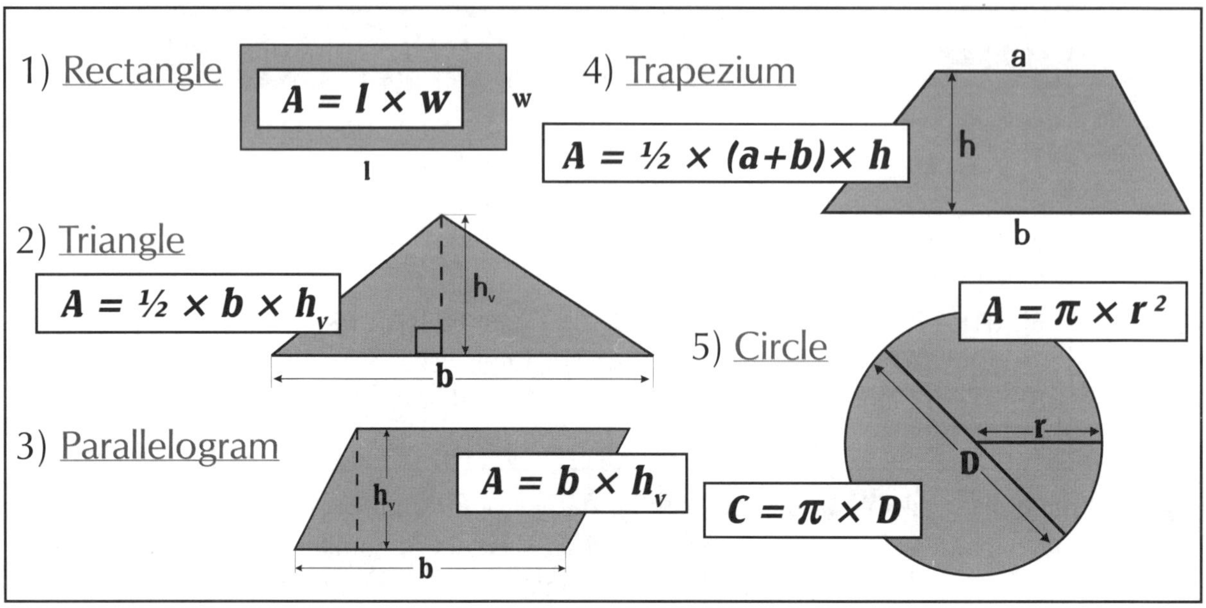

Q1 Calculate the area of the rectangle.

4cm, 6cm

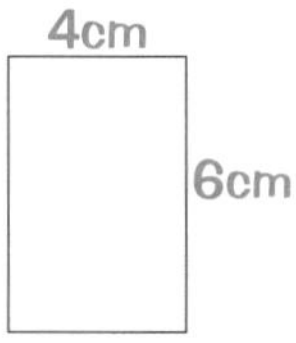

Q2 Calculate the area of the square.

5cm

Q3 A rectangular dining room, with a width equal to half its length, needs carpet tiling.
 a) Calculate the area of the floor, if its width is 12 m.
 b) If carpet tiles are 50 cm by 50 cm squares, calculate how many tiles will be required.
 c) If carpet tiles cost £4.99 per m², calculate the <u>cost</u> of tiling the dining room.

Q4 A modern glass sculpture is to be erected.
 It is made from glass in the shape of two mountain peaks.
 Calculate each <u>separate</u> area and hence
 find the <u>total</u> area of glass required.

T_1 16m

Tr_1 8m Tr_2 12m T_2

8m 8m 4m 8m

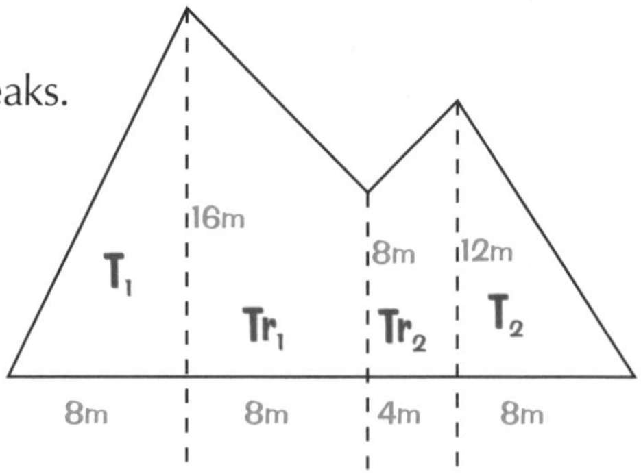

Work out the individual areas first, then add them together or take bits off to make the area you need. If only everything in life was this simple...

Q5 An attachment on a child's toy is made from plastic in the shape of an octagon with a square cut out. By counting squares or otherwise, find the area of plastic needed to make 4 of these attachments.

2cm, 4.24cm, 4cm, 2cm, 4cm, 2cm, 2cm, 4.24cm, 2cm

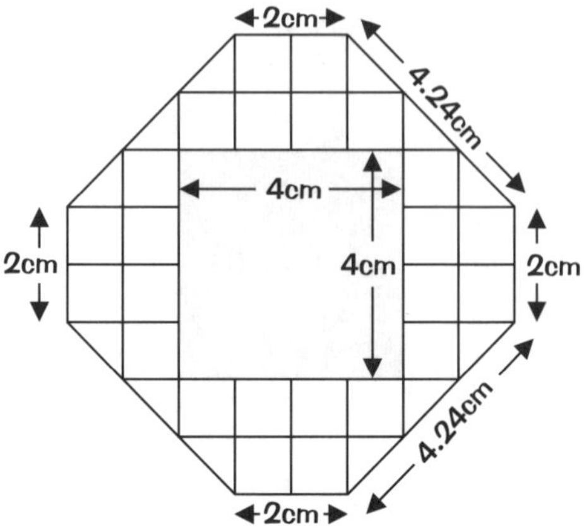

Questions on Areas

Q6 A metal blade for a craft knife is the shape of a <u>trapezium</u>. Calculate the area of the metal.

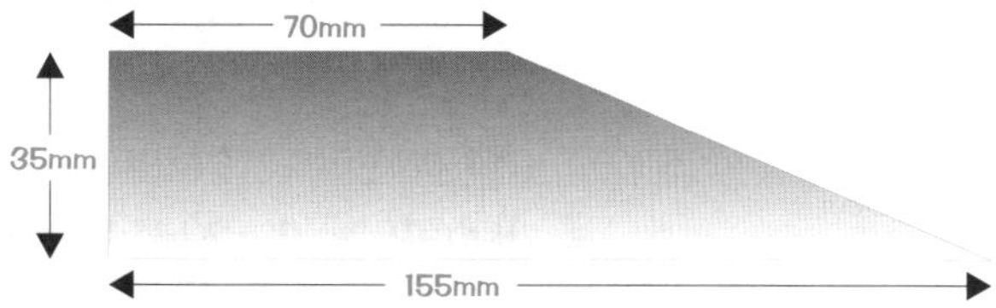

Q7 A cube bean bag is to be made out of material. If each side of the cube is to have edges of length 60 cm, how many <u>square metres</u> of material will be needed?

Q8 A rectangular lawn is to be made 48 m^2. If its width is 5 m, how long is it? How many rolls of turf 50 cm wide and 11 m long should be ordered to grass this area?

Q9 This parallelogram has an area of 4773 mm^2. How long is its <u>base</u>?

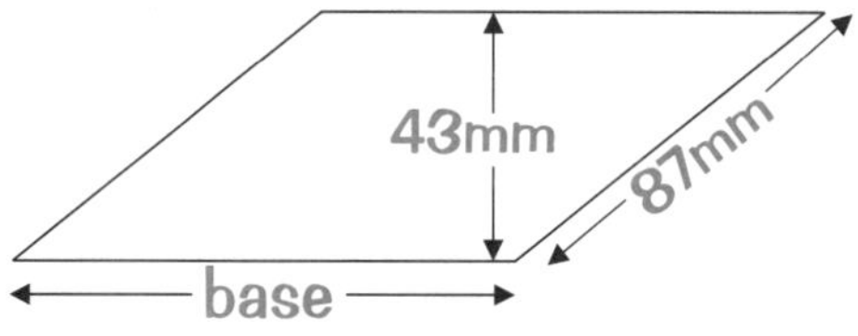

Q10 The area of a square is 9000 m^2.

a) What is the length of a <u>side</u>? (to 2 dp)

b) What is the <u>perimeter</u> of the square? (to 2 dp)

Q11 A simple tent is to be made in the shape of a triangular prism. The dimensions are shown in the diagram.

a) The two end faces are isosceles triangles. Find their areas.

b) The two sides and ground sheet are rectangles. Find their areas.

c) How much material is required to make this tent?

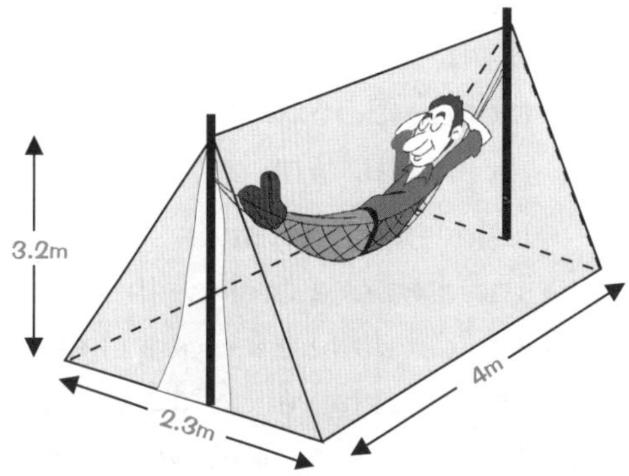

Q12 A fighter aircraft's wing is shown. Calculate its <u>area</u>, and its <u>perimeter</u>.

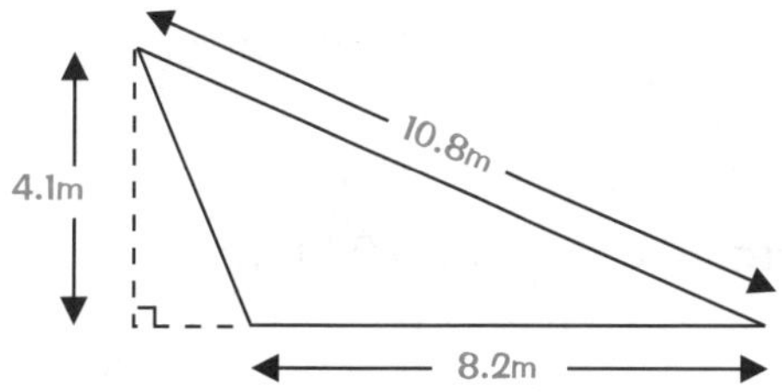

Q13 Calculate the area of a <u>rhombus</u> with diagonals 7 km and 11 km.

Q14 A hanging basket bracket of sheet metal is stamped out in a two-phase process:-
1st: The <u>outer triangle</u>, measuring 14.4 cm by 10 cm, is stamped out.
2nd: A smaller <u>inner triangle</u> measuring 5.76 cm by 4 cm is stamped out of the larger triangle.
How much metal makes up the finished bracket?

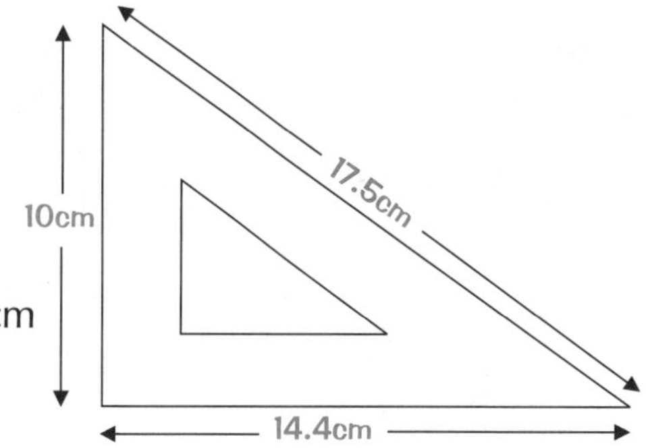

The <u>main thing</u> to remember is — you can <u>always</u> split up hard shapes into easy ones... like the "Top Five" on the last page, which you've already learnt.

Questions on Circles

You'll have no problems here if you learn these two formulas. Remember r stands for radius, D for Diameter and π for an annoying number slightly bigger than 3.

Circle Formulas

1) The Area A of a circle is $A = \pi \times r^2$

2) The Circumference C of a circle is $C = \pi \times D$

Q1 Find the circumference of each of the circles to 1 dp, using $\pi = 3.14$,

a) diameter = 20 m
b) diameter = 12 m
c) radius = 6 m
d) radius = 10 m.

Q2 Find the area of each of the circles to 3 dp, using $\pi = 3.142$,

a) diameter = 13.2 cm
b) diameter = 16.4 cm
c) radius = 3.56 m
d) radius = 6.15 m.

Q3 Using $\pi = 3.14$, find:

a) The area of a circle with radius = 6.12 m. Give your answer to 3 dp.
b) The circumference of a circle with radius = 7.2 m. Give your answer to 2 sf.
c) The circumference of a circle with diameter = 14.8 m. Give your answer to 1 dp.
d) The area of a circle with diameter = 4.246 cm. Give your answer to 3 dp.

Q4 Taking π as the value given by your calculator, find the radius of the following circles. All answers to 4 dp.

a) Circumference of 10 m.
b) Circumference of 0.02 mm.
c) Area of 36 cm^2.

Q5 Find the area and the perimeter of each of the shapes drawn here. Use $\pi = 3.14$.

a)

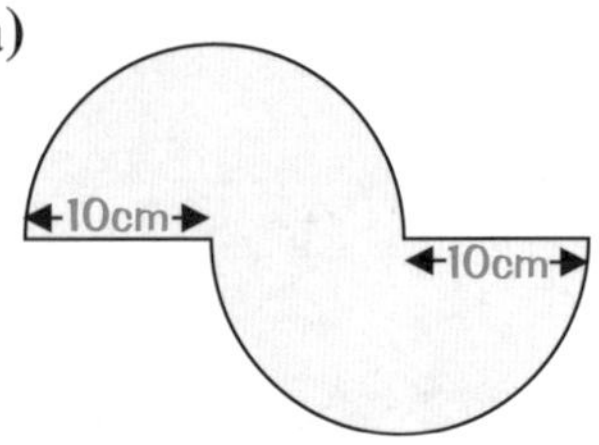

b)

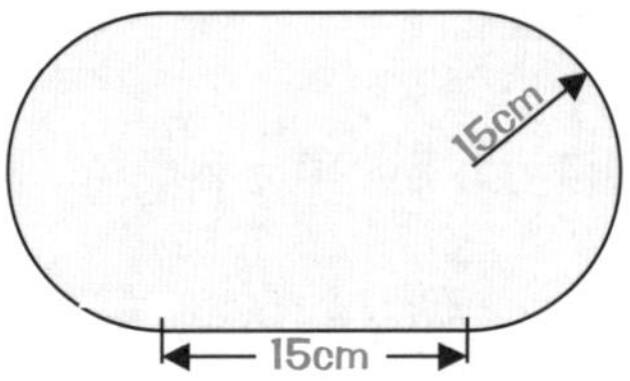

c)

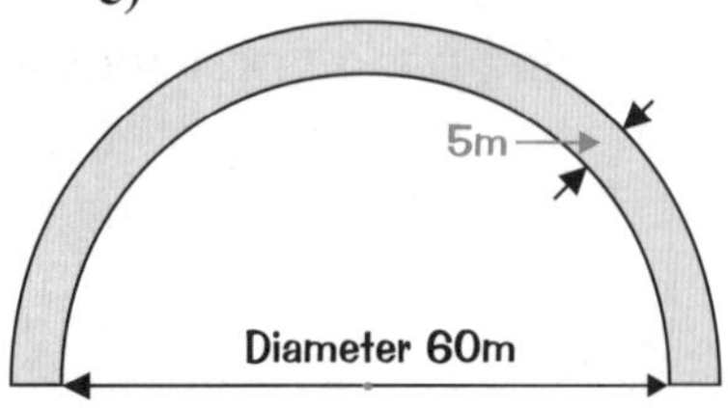

Q6 The circular lid on a jar of make-up has a diameter of 84 mm. Using $\pi = 3.14$, what is its circumference and area?

Q7 A circular pond has a circumference of 87.92 m. Using $\pi = 3.14$ calculate its diameter.

Questions on Area and Circumference

If you're having trouble remembering which formula is which, look at the r term — something with an r^2 in it has got to be an area, because it's a length times a length.

Q1 A car wheel plus tyre has a diameter of 58 cm. Using $\pi = 3.14$ what is the circumference of the tyre? How many revolutions (to the nearest whole number) will the tyre make in travelling 1000 m?

Q2 The pond in Question 7 on P.74 has a 1 m wide concrete path around its circumference. Calculate the area of the path.

Q3 A rug in front of a fire is in the shape of a semicircle. It has a diameter equal to the width of the fire hearth, which is 1.8 m wide. using $\pi = 3.14$ calculate the area of the rug, to 3 sf.

Q4 The rug in Q3 is to have non-slip braid attached around its perimeter to stop it moving. How many metres of braid will be required to do the job? (Give answer to 3 sf.)

Q5 A child's sandpit is circular, and made from hard PVC. It has a depth of 10 cm and a diameter of 450 mm. ($\pi = 3.14$)

a) Calculate the surface area of the sandpit's floor both in mm^2 and m^2 to 2 dp.

b) A red stripe is to be painted all of the way round the inside face of the sandpit. How long would the stripe be in mm?

c) If the stripe were to be 20 mm wide, what area of red paint would be visible?

Q6 A yo-yo is made up of two identical halves. Each half is circular with a circular spindle protruding from it. The two spindles are glued together and the string is tied on and wrapped around it 50 times.

a) The central spindle has a diameter of 1.2 cm. What is its circumference?

b) Using your answer from **a)**, find approximately how long the yo-yo's string should be if 6 cm is allowed for a finger loop, and 5 cm is allowed to tie it to the spindle.

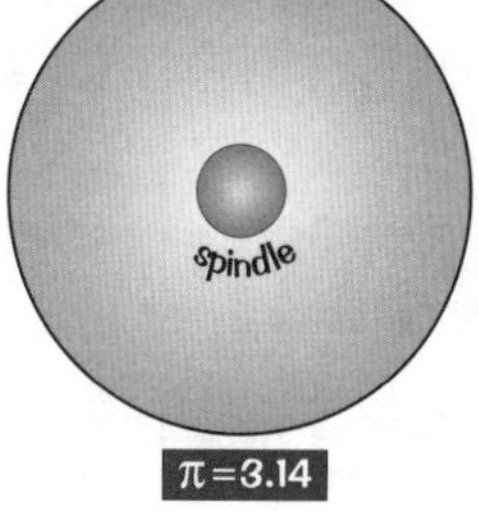

Q7 A Big Wheel at a fairground has a diameter of 36 m.

a) How far does a passenger travel in one revolution?

b) If the wheel at full capacity has a speed of 6 revolutions per minute, and a ride lasts for 4 minutes, how far does a passenger travel? ($\pi = 3.14$)

Q8 The base of a triangle is equal in length to the circumference of a circle which has a radius of 5 cm. The triangle and the circle also have an equal area. What is the height of the triangle? (Again, $\pi = 3.14$)

Q9 The diagram shows the spool on a cassette with recording tape wrapped around it. The ring of tape has an internal radius of 11 mm and external radius of 23 mm.

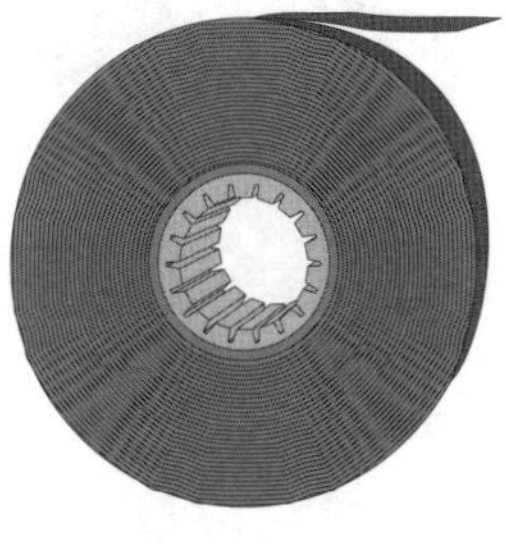

a) Find the area of the side view of tape in cm^2.

b) If the recording tape is 50 m long, how thick is it?

c) If half of the cassette is played, half of the tape is unwound from one spool to the other. Calculate the external radius of the tape now occupying the original spool.

Questions on Perimeters and Areas

For perimeters, the Big Blob Method is the best way to be sure you've got all the sides.

PERIMETER is the distance all the way around the outside of a 2D shape

Always use the BIG BLOB method:
1) Put a BIG BLOB at one corner, then go around the shape.
2) Write down the length of every side as you go.
3) Even sides that seem to have no length given — you must work them out.
4) Keep going until you get back to the BIG BLOB. Then add up all the sides.

Q1 A sail is the triangular shape shown in the diagram.

a) What is its perimeter?

b) A smaller sail is kept in a locker to be used on windier days. Its area is 26.8 m^2, its width is 2.06 m and it is also isosceles.

i) Find its height.

ii) Find its perimeter.

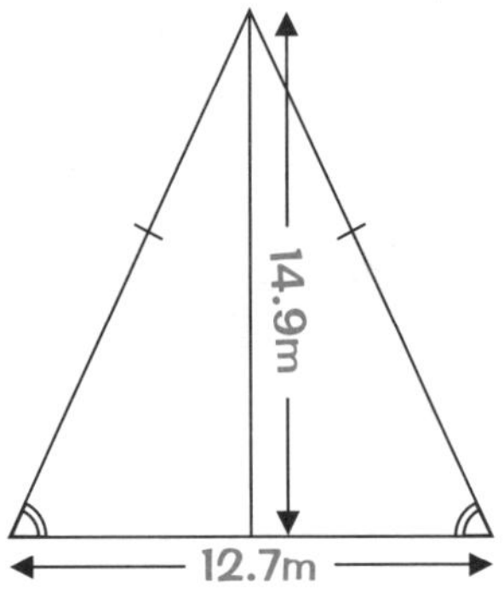

Q2 In front of a toilet is a special mat that fits snugly around the base.

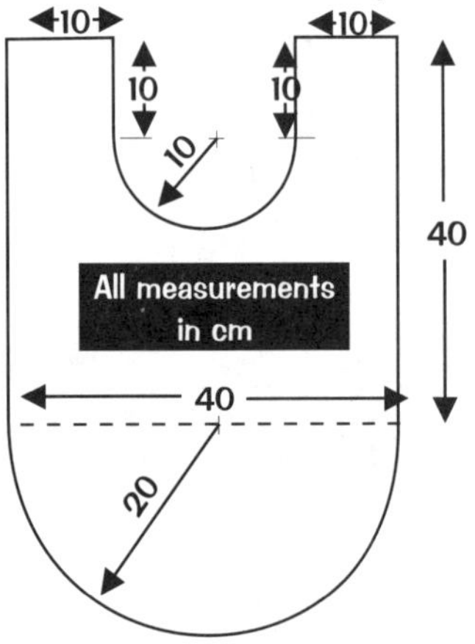

Using the diagram opposite:

a) Find the amount of braid needed to be stitched all round its edge.

b) Find the area of fluffy wool carpet it will cover when placed in front of the toilet.

You'll find the next few quite easy if you work out the small area first and then take it off the big one.

Q3 Find the shaded areas for each of the following:

a)

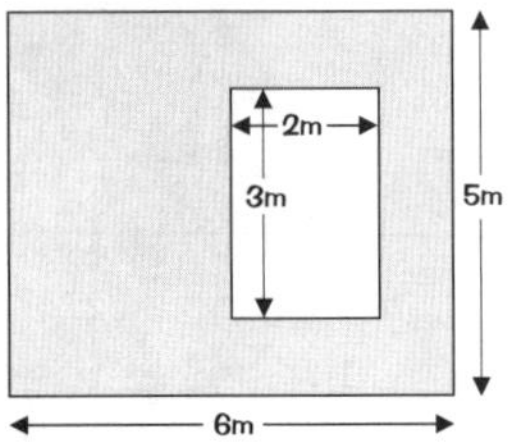

b)

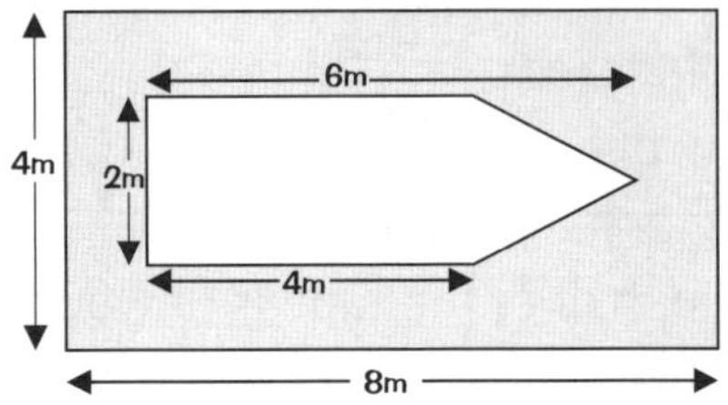

c)

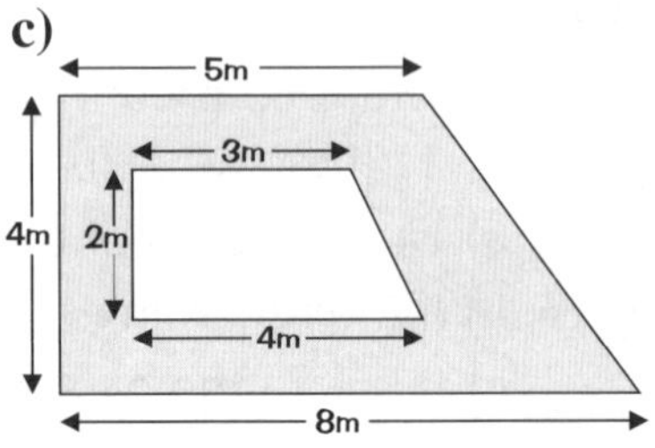

Questions on Volume or Capacity

***Capacity** is **exactly** the same thing as **volume** — simple as that. And things will get even simpler once you've learnt the two formulas below.*

VOLUME FORMULAS

1) Volume of cuboid =
Length × Width × Height

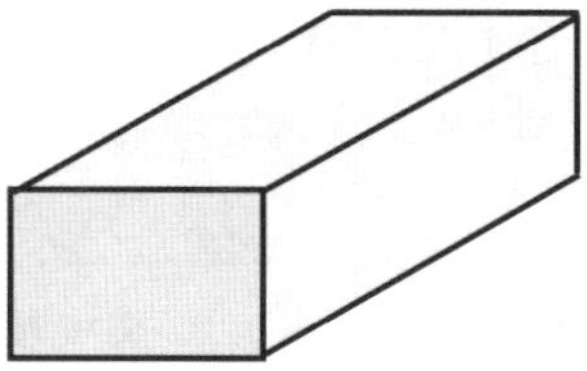

2) Volume of any prism =
Cross-sectional area × Length

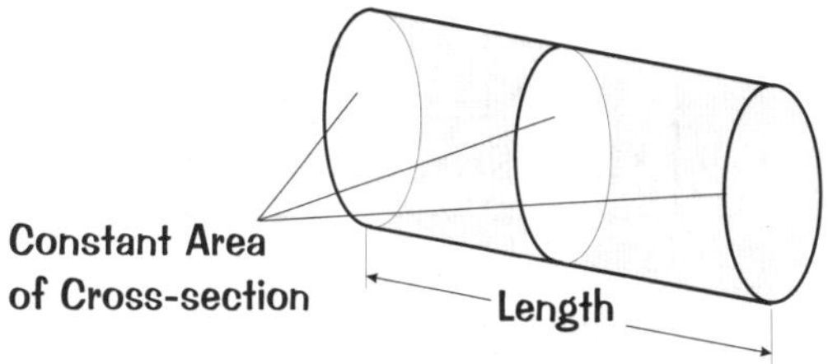

Contrary to popular belief, there isn't anything that complicated about prisms — they're only solids with the same shape all the way through. The only bit that sometimes takes a bit longer is finding the cross-sectional area. (Back a few pages for a reminder of areas.)

Q1 A coffee mug is a cylinder closed at one end. The internal radius is 7 cm with an internal height of 9 cm.

a) If $\pi = 3.14$, find the volume of liquid the mug can hold.

b) If 1200 cm^3 of liquid is poured into the mug, find the depth to the nearest whole mm.

Q2 An unsharpened pencil can be thought of as a regular hexagonal prism with a cylinder of graphite along the axis of the prism.

a) By considering a hexagon to be made up of six equilateral triangles, calculate the area of the cross-section of the hexagonal prism, shown.

b) Find the area of wood in the cross-section.

c) If the pencil is 20 cm long what is the volume of wood in the pencil?

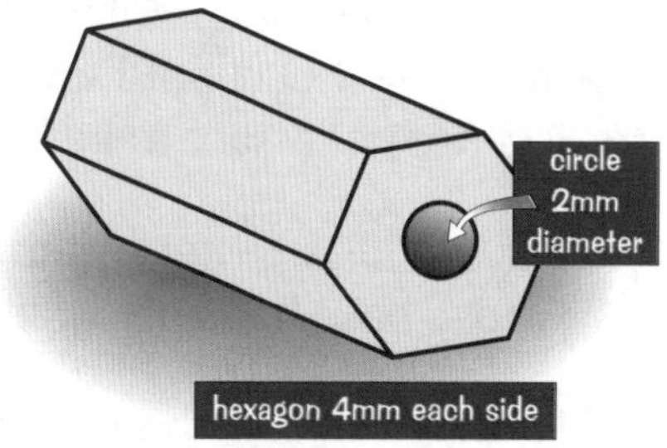

Q3 A pipe disperses oil into cylindrical barrels with internal height 1 m and radius 25 cm.

a) Calculate the volume of oil contained in a completely full barrel, in cm^3.

b) The lid consists of a circular plastic insert of the same radius as that of the barrel and of depth 22 mm.
Calculate the volume of oil lost if the lid is inserted into a completely full barrel.

c) Discover how long it takes to sufficiently fill a barrel so that none is lost by inserting the lid, if the pipe dispenses oil at the rate of 43.5 litres per minute.

Q4 Nosher's Xmas Hamper is a wicker basket in the shape of a regular pentagonal prism. The hamper has internal dimensions of 40 cm long sides and a depth of 40 cm. What volume of delicious seasonal food could be fitted within this space?

Q5 A tree trunk can be thought of as a circular prism with a height of 1.7 m. If the trunk has radius 60 cm what volume of wood is this in m^3?

Questions on Solids and Nets

Before you go any further ***— make sure you know these 4 facts...***

Surface Area and Nets

1) SURFACE AREA only applies to solid 3-D objects. It's the TOTAL AREA of all the OUTER SURFACES added together.
2) There is no simple formula for surface area — you have to work out each side in turn and then ADD THEM ALL TOGETHER.
3) A NET is just A SOLID SHAPE folded out FLAT.
4) SURFACE AREA OF SOLID = AREA OF NET.

There are 4 nets that you need to know inside out... so to speak: 1) Triangular Prism, 2) Cube, 3) Cuboid, 4) Pyramid. I reckon you shouldn't read any further till you're 100% happy with them.

Q1 The net shown will fold to make a cube. Only one flap is shown. Copy the diagram.

a) Put an X in each corner that touches Y when the cube is made up.

b) Put an F where the flap will join one face to another, when the cube is made up.

c) Put on the other flaps necessary to glue the cube together.

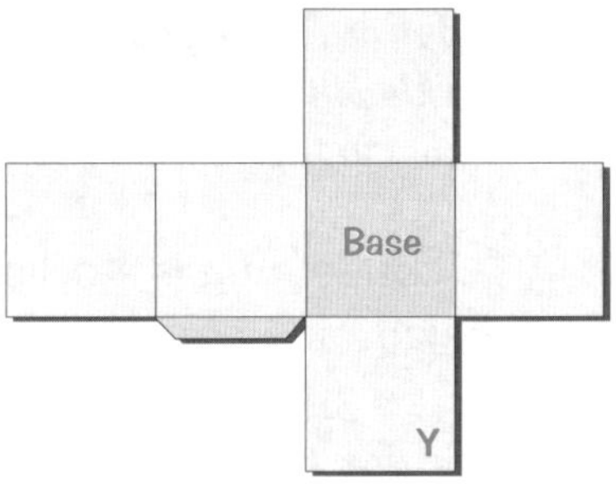

Q2 Draw an accurate 2-dimensional net that would fold to make the 3-D cuboid shown (diagram is not full size). It is not necessary to include flaps.

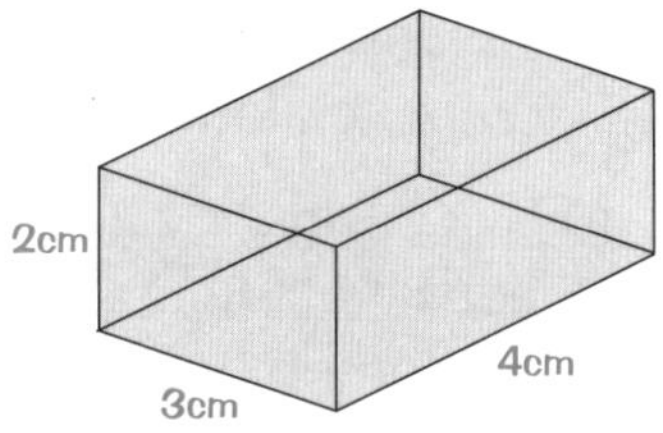

Q3 Draw a full size net (without flaps) of a square-based pyramid whose base has sides of length 3 cm.

Q4 Draw accurately the net of a regular tetrahedron, with sufficient flaps to glue it together.

Q5 **a)** What shape is the base of the cuboid shown opposite?

b) Which edges are the same length as DE?

c) Which lengths equal CE?

d) Which lengths equal the diagonal DG?

e) How many vertices does the cuboid have?

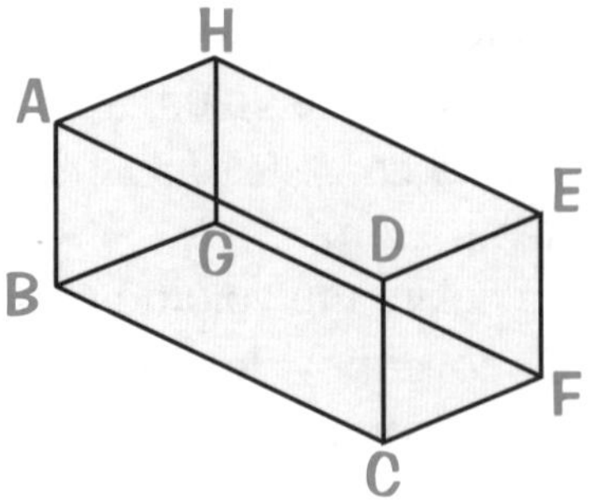

Q6 Draw a circular cone.

a) How many vertices does it have?

b) How many edges?

Q7 An equilateral triangular prism has a tetrahedron placed on top of it, as shown. For this combined solid,

a) How many edges does it have?

b) How many vertices?

c) How many faces?

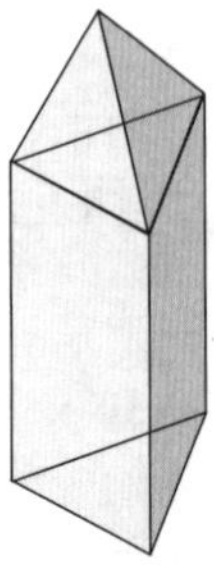

Questions on Geometry

Angle Rules — you've already met a couple of these in the Polygons bit... and here are another 7 to go at. You can't get away without knowing these, I'm afraid, so get learning.

1) Angles in a triangle add up to 180°

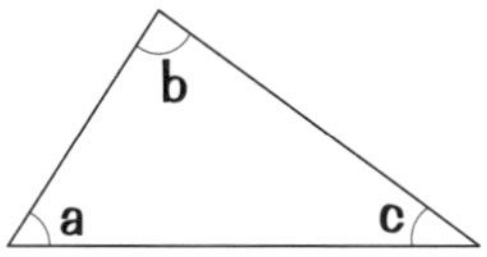

2) Angles in a 4-sided shape add up to 360°

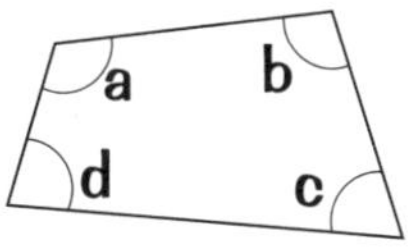

3) Angles round a point add up to 360°

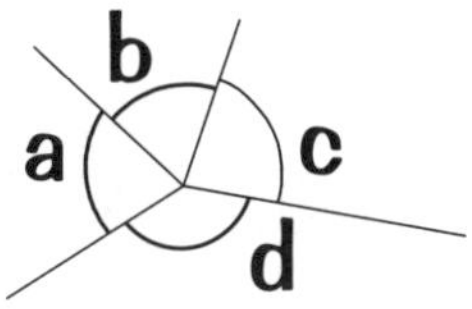

4) When a line crosses TWO PARALLEL LINES, the two bunches of angles are the same

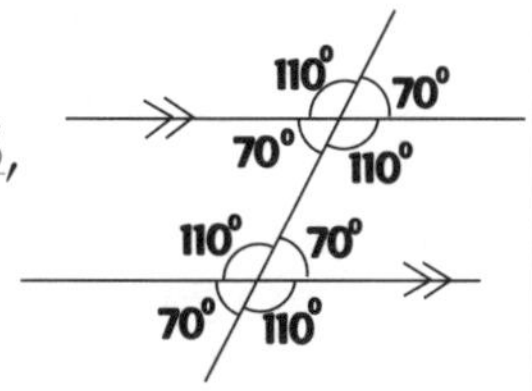

5) Angles on a straight line add up to 180°

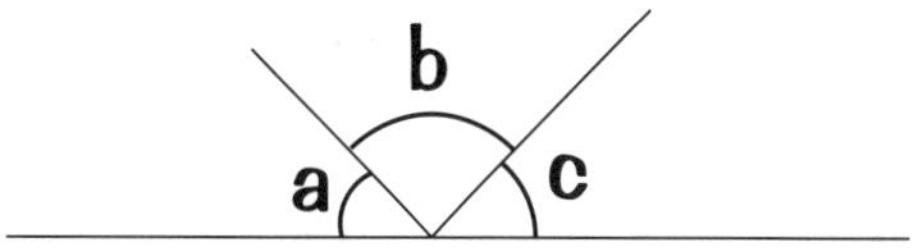

6) ISOSCELES TRIANGLES have two sides the same and two angles the same

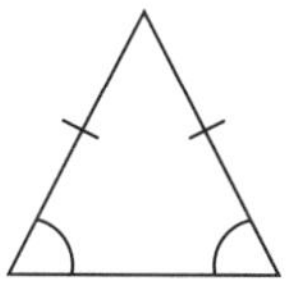

7) In an IRREGULAR POLYGON,

Sum of Exterior angles = 360°

Sum of Interior angles = (n – 2) × 180°

(n is the number of sides)

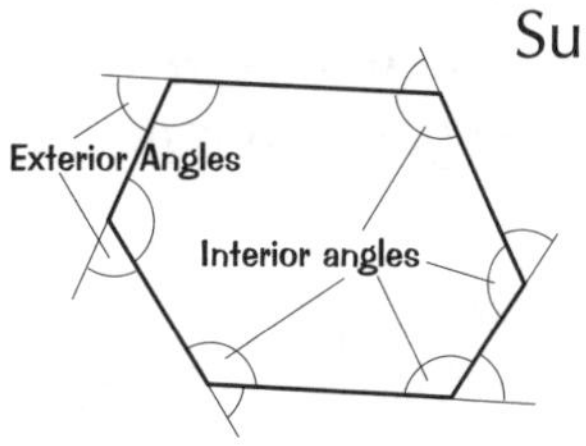

For the following diagrams, find the lettered angles. LM is a straight line.

Q1 a)

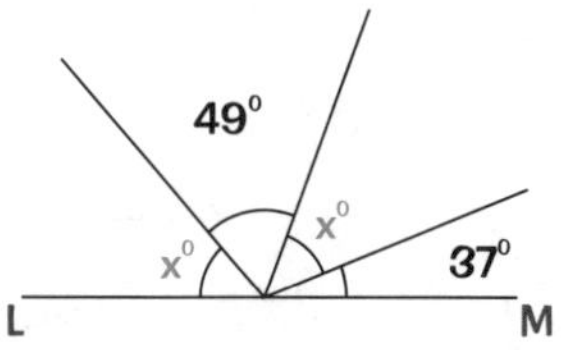

b)

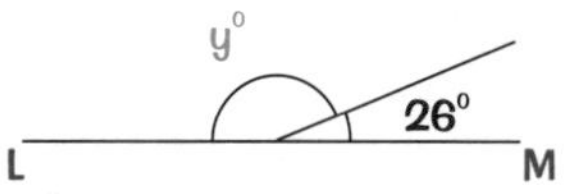

c)

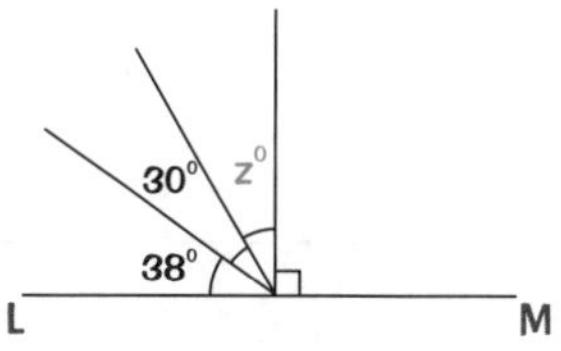

d)

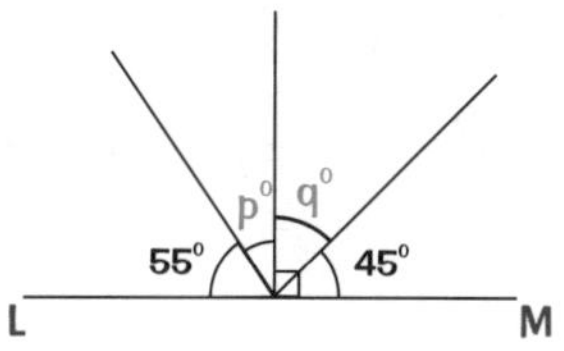

Q2 a)

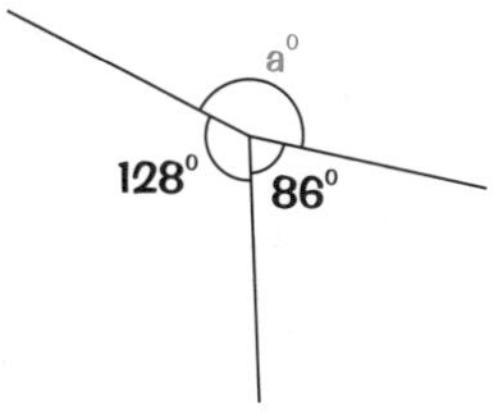

b)

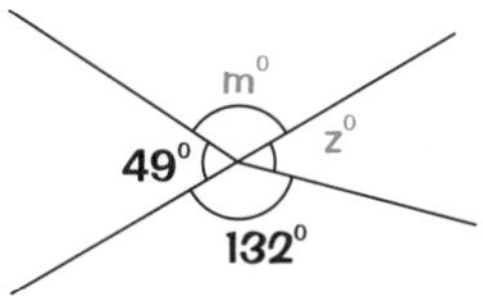

c)

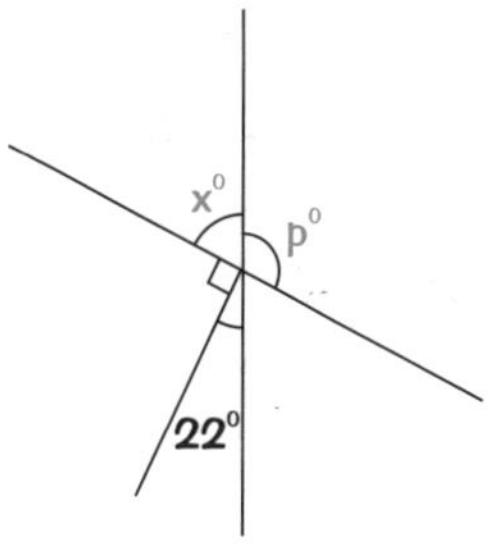

d)

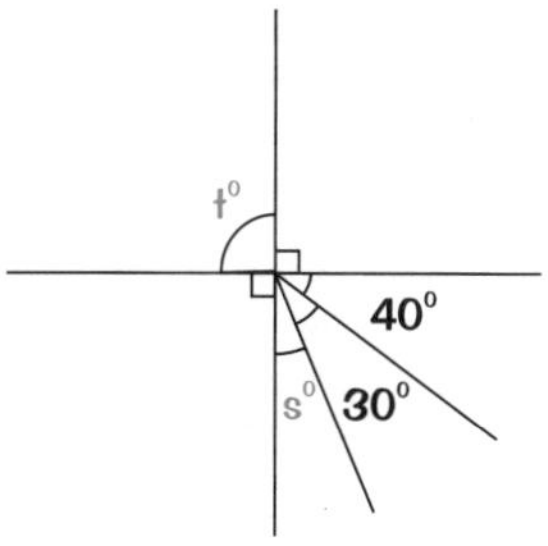

Questions on Geometry

This page is a bit dull — just lots of boring angles... still, that's geometry for you. Oh and by the way, you've got to work the angles out — don't try and sneakily measure them, they're probably drawn wrong anyway...

For the following diagrams, find the lettered angles. LM is a straight line.

Q3 a)

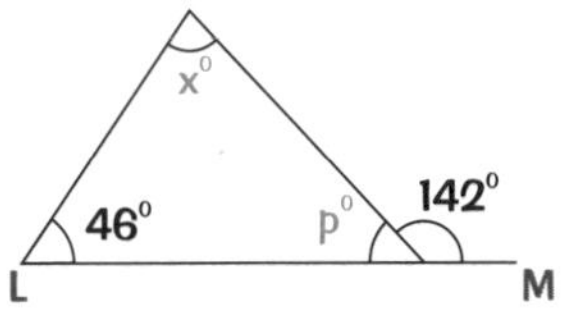

b)

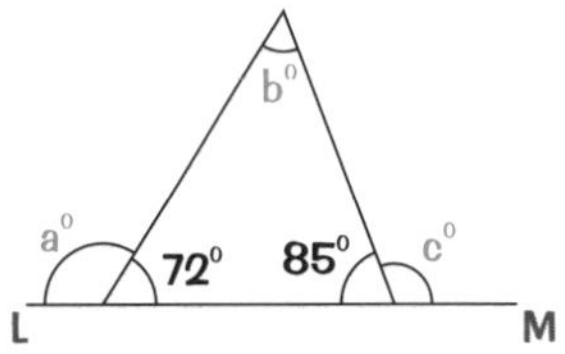

c)

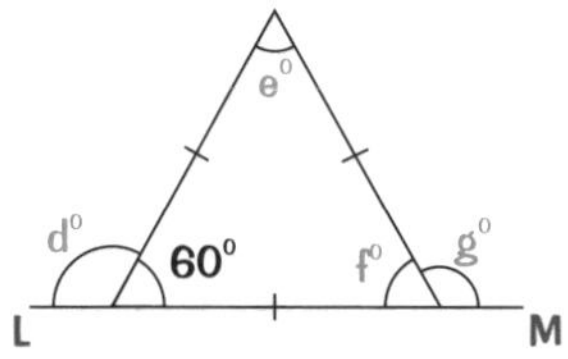

d)

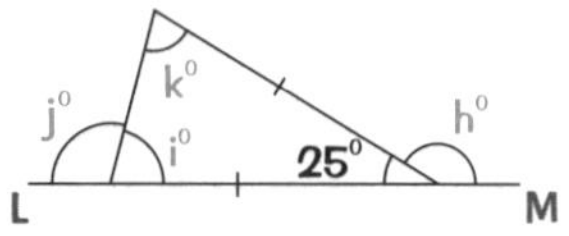

Q4 a)

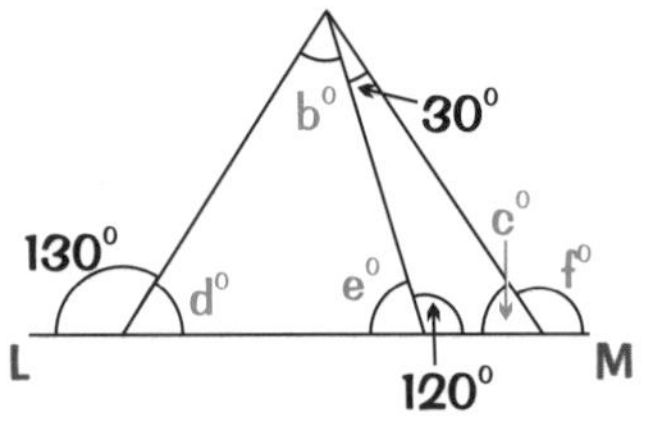

b)

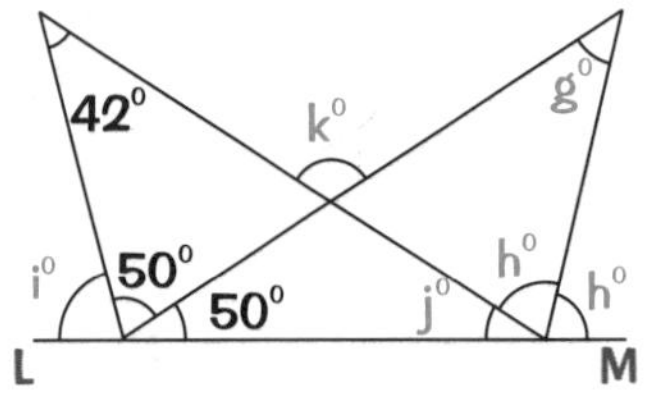

c)

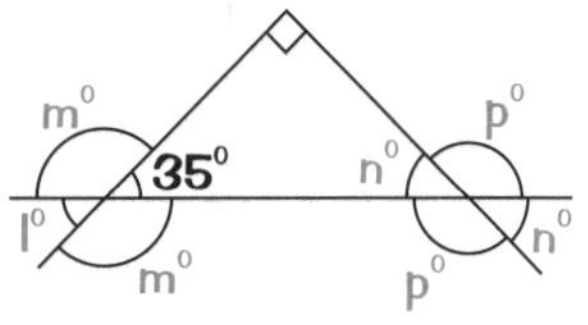

Keep an eye out for parallel lines — they'll help no end... as long as you can remember the angle rules, of course...

Q5 a)

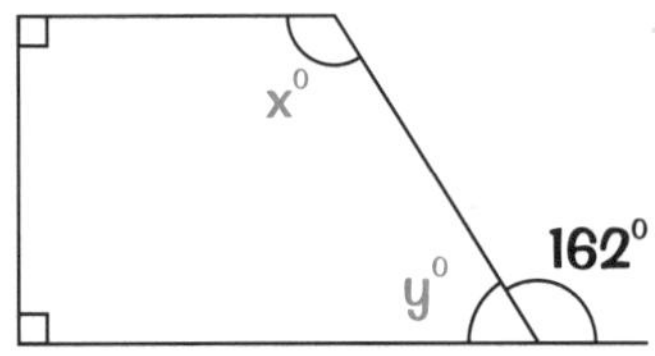

b)

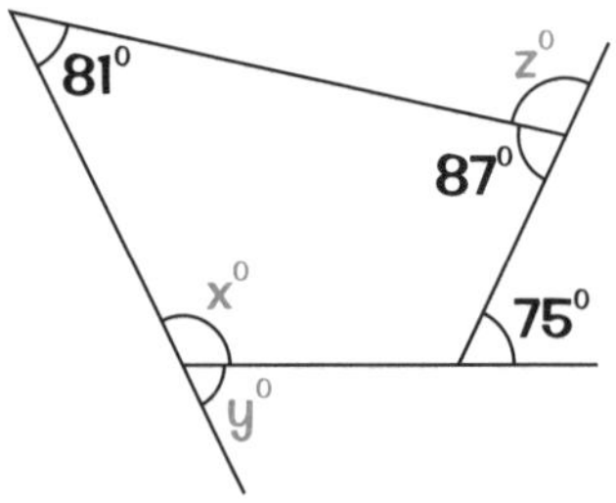

c)

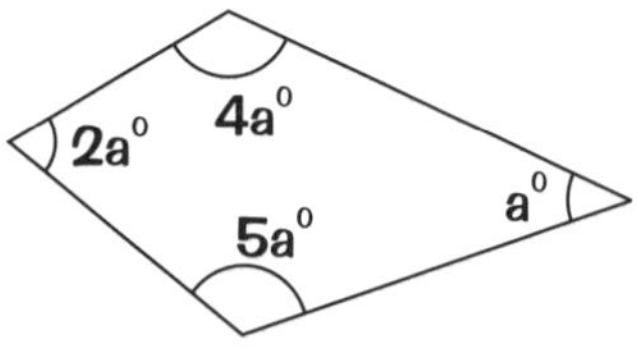

Q6 a)

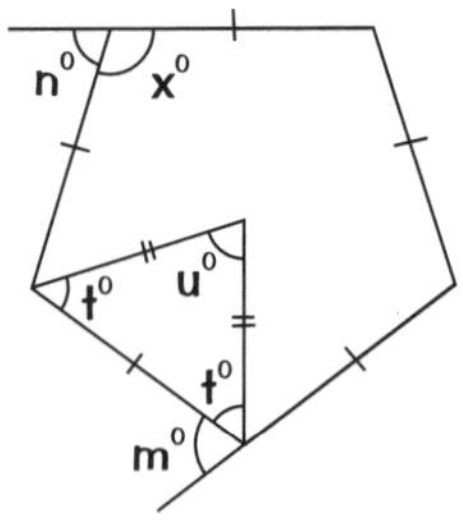

b)

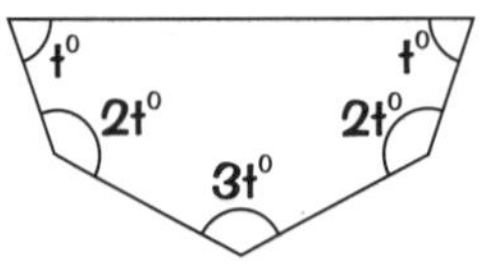

c)

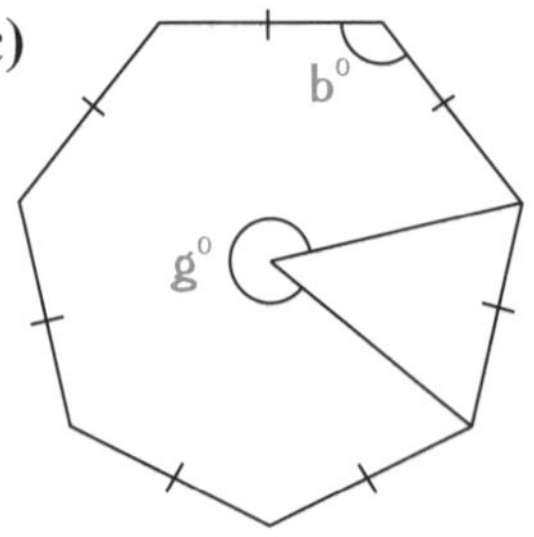

d)

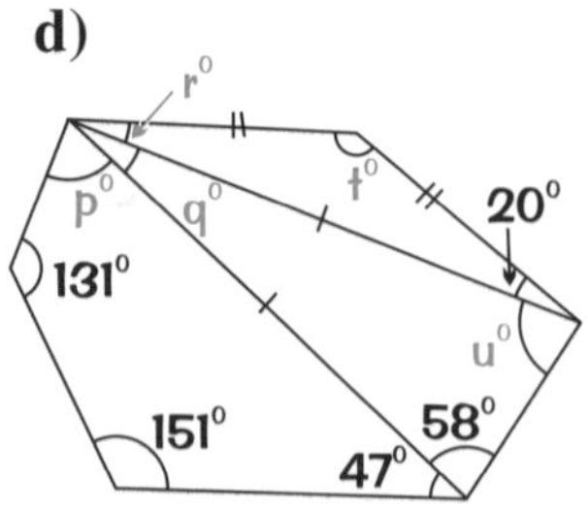

Q7 a)

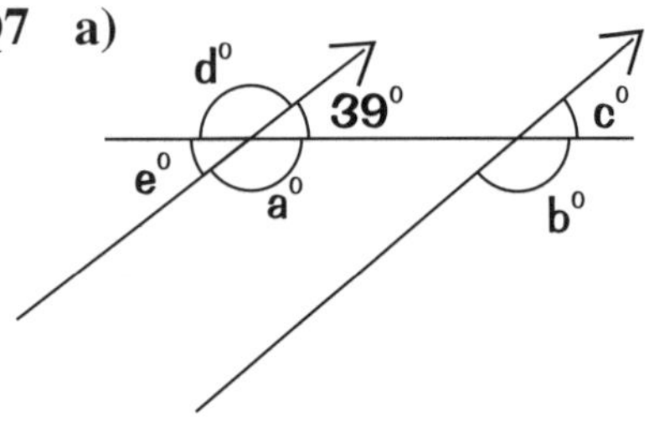

b)

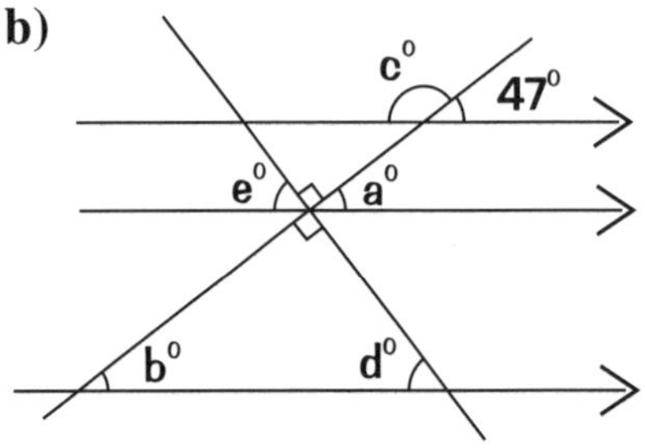

c)

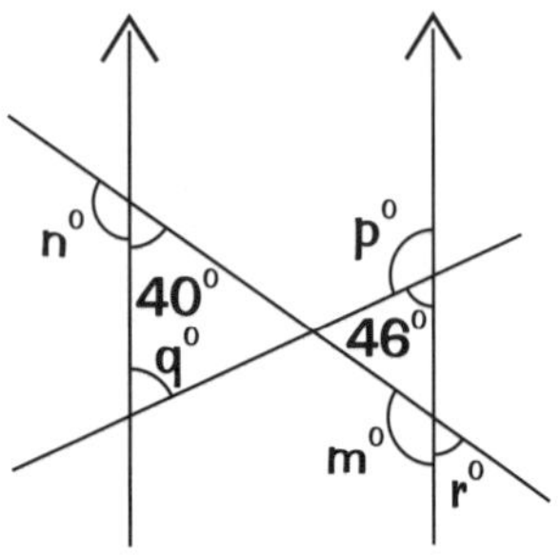

Questions on Geometry

Don't forget — with geometry, the more you do it, the easier it gets... honestly.

For the following diagrams, find the lettered angles.

Q8 **a)**

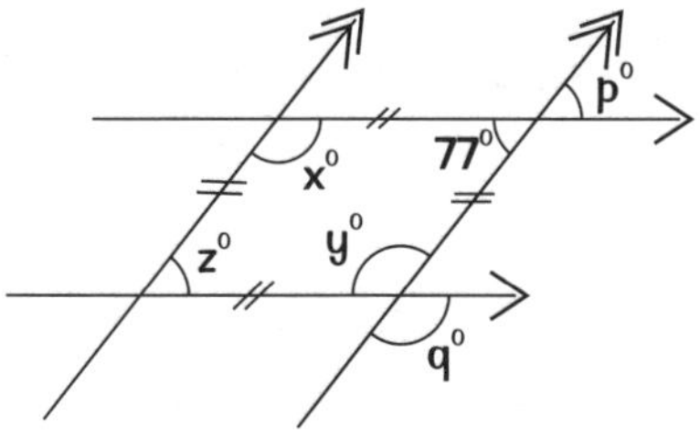

b)

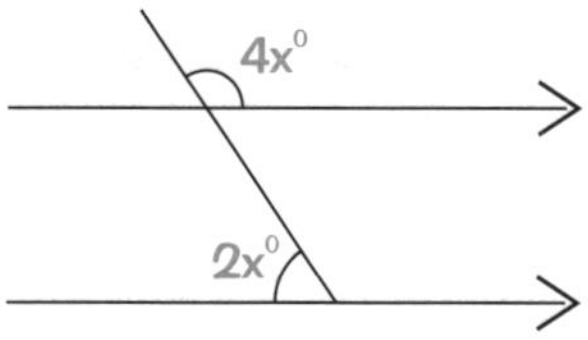

c)

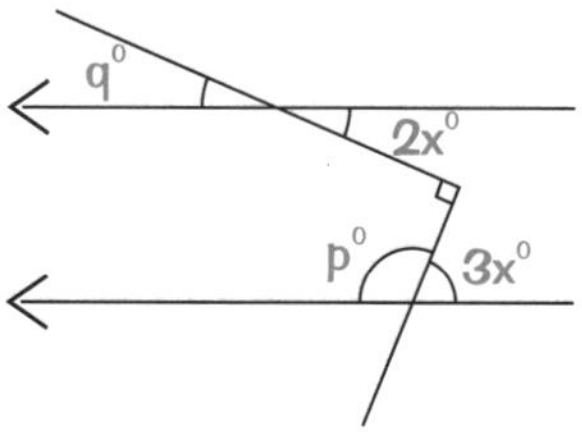

Q9 **a)**

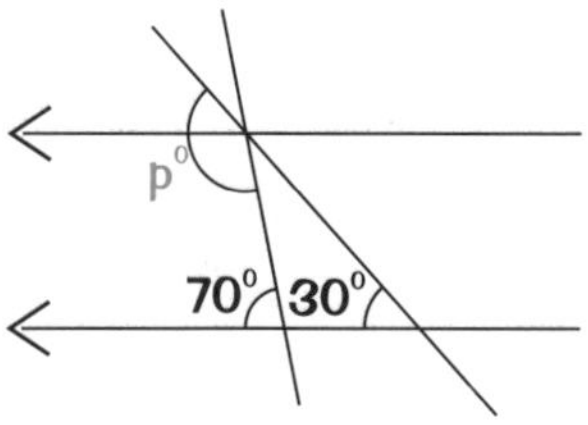

b)

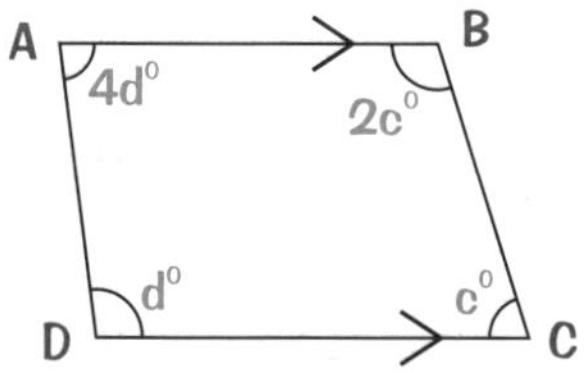

c)

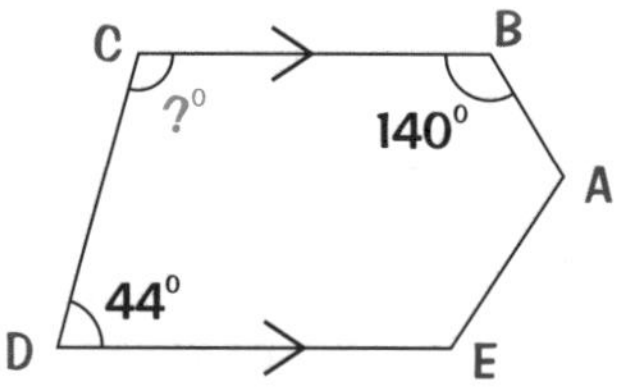

Q10 a)

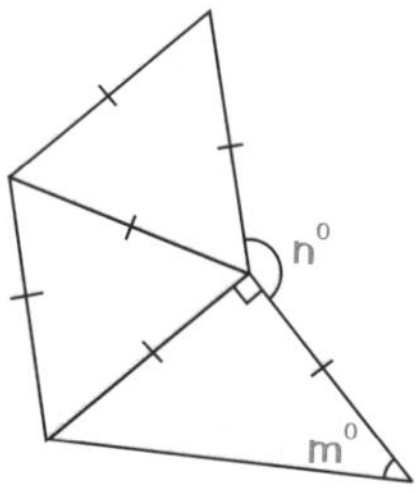

b)

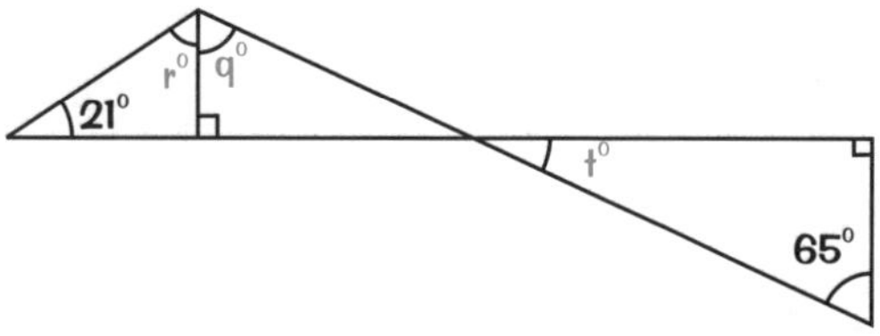

c)

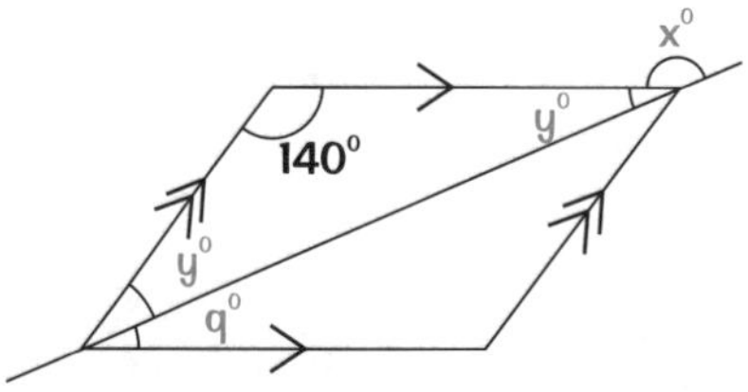

Q11 ABCD is a trapezium with AB parallel to DC. Diagonal DB bisects ADC. Show that ABD is isosceles.

Q12 Given that one angle of a parallelogram is 37°, what are the sizes of the others?

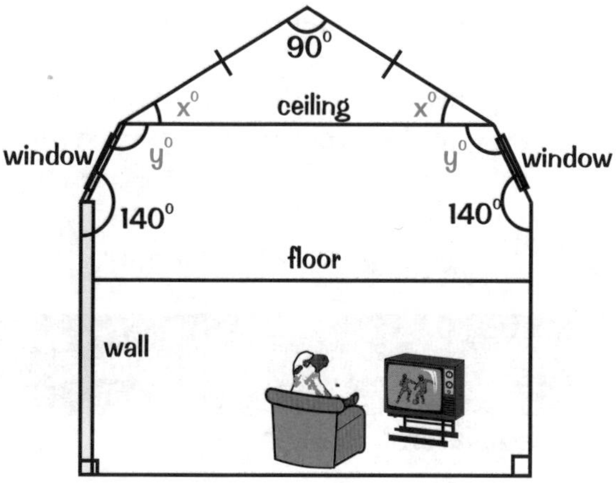

Q13 A "MANSARD roof" allows rooms to be put into the roof, with normal windows. In the drawing opposite, the wall meets the roof at 140°. The roof with the window meets the inner ceiling at y°. The peak of the roof is 90°. Calculate x and y, as shown in the drawing.

Geometry is really jam-packed with angle rules — and you won't get anywhere without them. It's not enough to be able to use them — you've got to remember them, too.

Questions on Regular Polygons

The one thing they're guaranteed to ask you about is Interior and Exterior Angles — you'd better get learning those formulas...

A POLYGON is a many-sided shape. A REGULAR polygon is one where ALL THE SIDES AND ANGLES ARE THE SAME.

You need to know these two formulas:

1) EXTERIOR ANGLE = 360° ÷ No. of Sides
2) INTERIOR ANGLE = 180° – EXTERIOR ANGLE

Q1 What sort of triangles occur in a regular hexagon when each vertex is joined to the centre by a straight line?

Q2 What sort of triangles occur in every regular polygon (except a hexagon), when each vertex is joined to the centre by a straight line?

Q3 Using a compass, construct a regular hexagon with sides equal to 3 cm.

Q4 Using a compass, construct an equilateral triangle with sides 3 cm. What angle is at each vertex?

These compass ones are a bit fiddly — the only way to make sure you can do them is to keep trying. If you can't do them in the comfort of your own home, you'll stand no chance in the Exam.

Q5 What formula links interior with exterior angles?

Q6 What formula could be used to work out the exterior angle of a regular polygon if the number of sides of the regular polygon is known?

Q7 Sketch a regular hexagon and draw in all its lines of symmetry. State the order of rotational symmetry.

Q8 Draw in all the lines of symmetry on this pentagon. State the order of rotational symmetry.

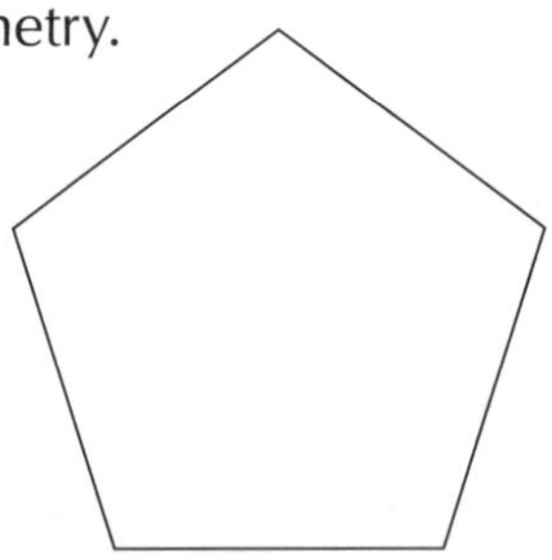

Q9 Complete the following table:

Name	Sides	Lines of Symmetry	Order of Rotational Symmetry
Equilateral Triangle			
Square		4	
Regular Pentagon			
Regular Hexagon	6		
Regular Heptagon	7		
Regular Octagon			8
Regular Decagon	10		

Questions on Regular Polygons

Q10 In each of the pentagons, all the sides are of equal length, two of the angles are 90° and the other interior angles are m, m, and r degrees.

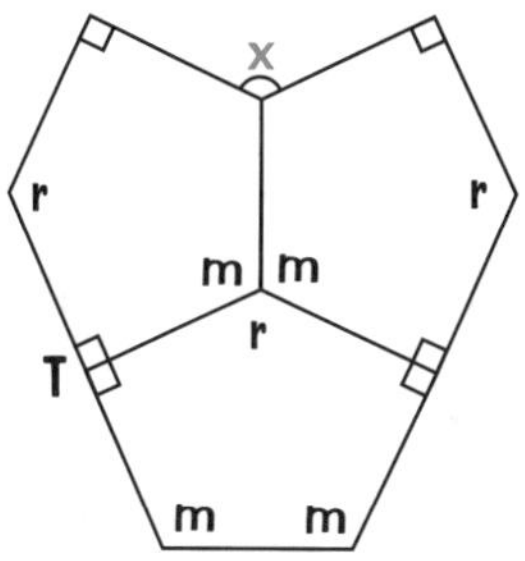

a) Explain in <u>two</u> different ways why $2m + r = 360°$.

b) What is the exterior angle x?

c) Copy the diagram and add two more pentagons (by tracing through) so that the point T is completely surrounded and the whole figure forms part of a tessellation. Label all the angles of the new pentagons.

Q11 A square and a regular hexagon are placed adjacent to each other.

a) What is the <u>size</u> of ∠PQW?

b) What is the <u>size</u> of ∠PRW?

c) How many sides has the <u>regular polygon</u> that has ∠PQW as one of its angles?

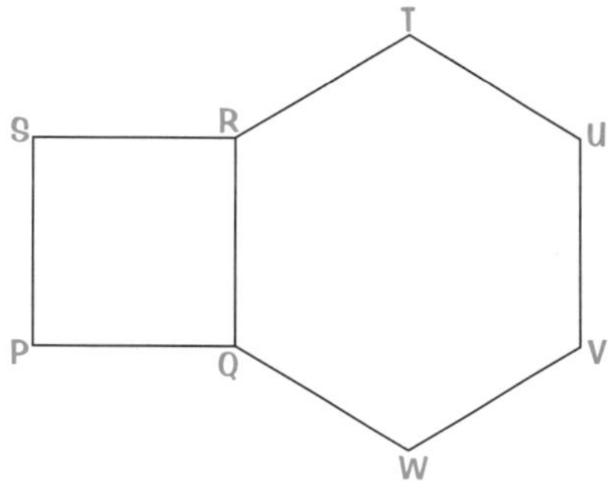

Q12 Here is a <u>regular decagon</u>.
Calculate:

a) ∠AOB

b) ∠OBA

c) ∠ABC

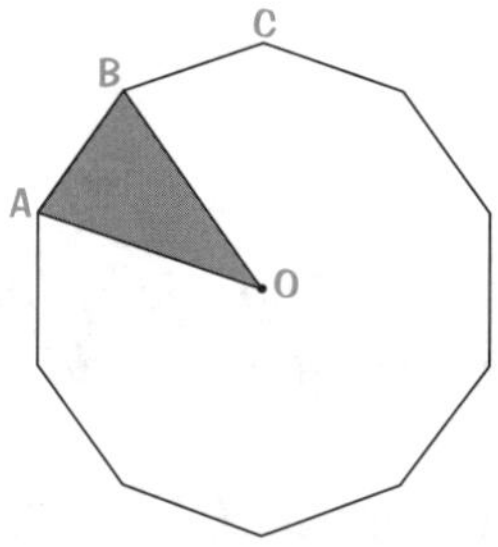

Q13 In a regular <u>7-sided</u> polygon, what is the size of one interior angle? Is it:

a) $128\frac{4}{7}°$ **b)** 135° **c)** 120° **d)** $112\frac{2}{7}°$ or **e)** 140°?

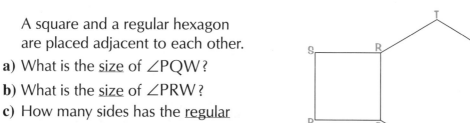

You'll need to brush up on your Trigonometry for this one — yeah, bit dull innit. Still, you've got to do these things for the Exam, so get scribbling...

Q14 A <u>regular hexagon</u> has a perimeter of 48 cm. What is the distance between two of the opposite sides, is it

a) 13.9 cm **b)** 18.5 cm **c)** 12.2 cm **d)** 15.7 cm or **e)** 14.2 cm?

Q15 An <u>irregular pentagon</u> has interior angles of 100°, 104°, 120°. If the other two angles are equal, what is their size?

Q16 A regular polygon has an <u>interior</u> angle of 160°. Calculate

a) the size of each exterior angle

b) how many sides it has.

Q17 The <u>exterior</u> angle of a <u>regular</u> polygon is 24°. How many sides does it have?

Q18 a) Find the size of the interior angles of a <u>regular</u> 24-sided polygon.

b) From this answer calculate one <u>exterior</u> angle and show that the <u>sum</u> of the exterior angles equals 360°.

Questions on Circle Geometry

There's loads of vital things to know about circles — so start practising and find out how much you know.

Q1 If AB is the <u>diameter</u> of the circle and O is the centre, find the angles:

a) ADB
b) ABD
c) ADC
d) ACD
e) CBD
f) BAC

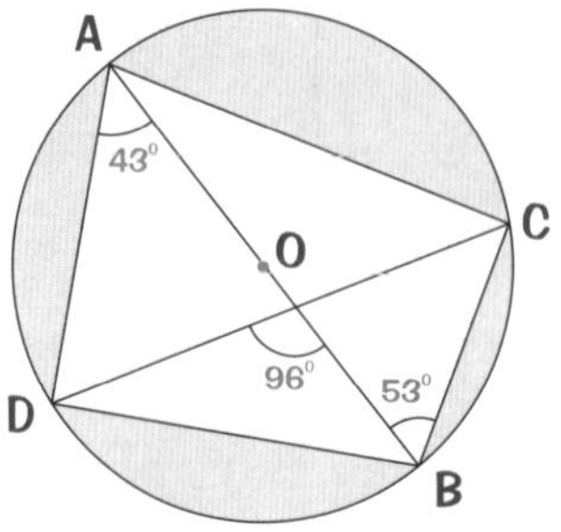

Q2 In each of the following parts find the angle asked for and say <u>why</u> this is the answer.

a) ∠ABC
b) ∠BCA
c) ∠BCT
d) ∠BDC

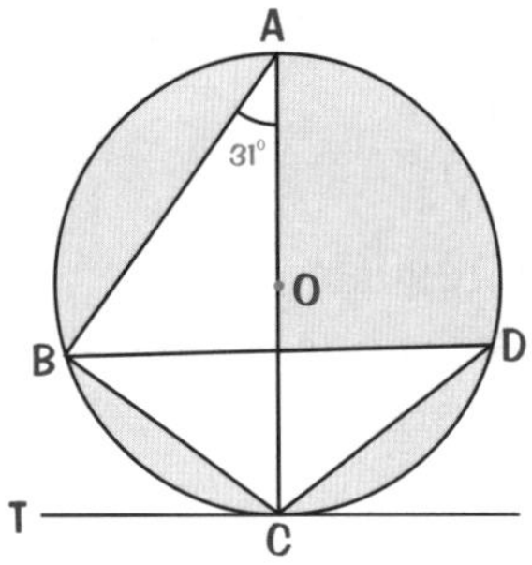

Make sure you remember your <u>triangle</u> stuff — you'll need it for some of these. Especially the one about the <u>interior</u> angles of a triangle <u>always</u> adding up to <u>180°</u>.

Q3 Find all the angles shown in the diagram. Give reasons for <u>at least three</u> of the angles being what they are.

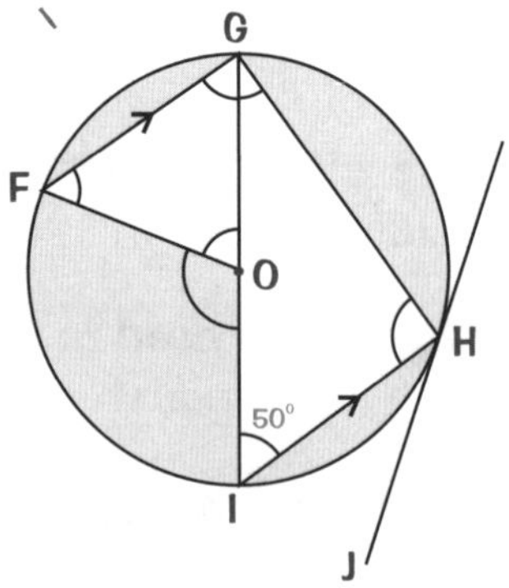

Q4 **a)** In the circle on the left, calculate the length CD.

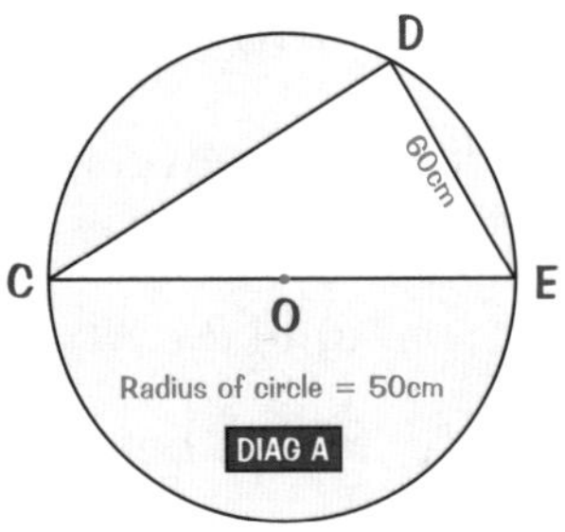

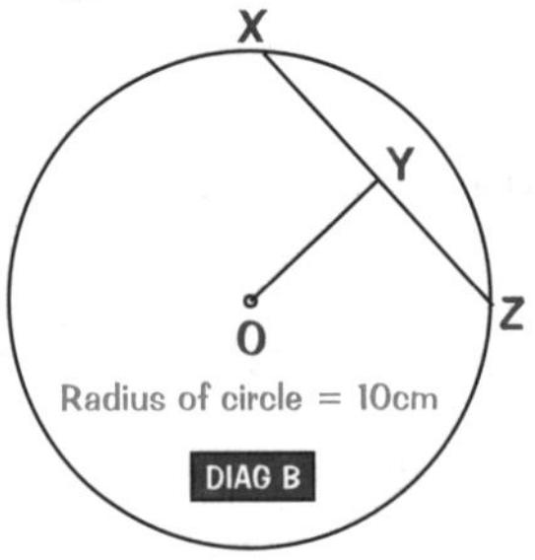

b) In the circle on the right, calculate the length OY if the chord XZ is 16 cm long.

Q5 **a)** State the length BD in the diagram on the right.

b) Calculate the angle COD.

c) State the angle COB.

d) Find the angle CAB.

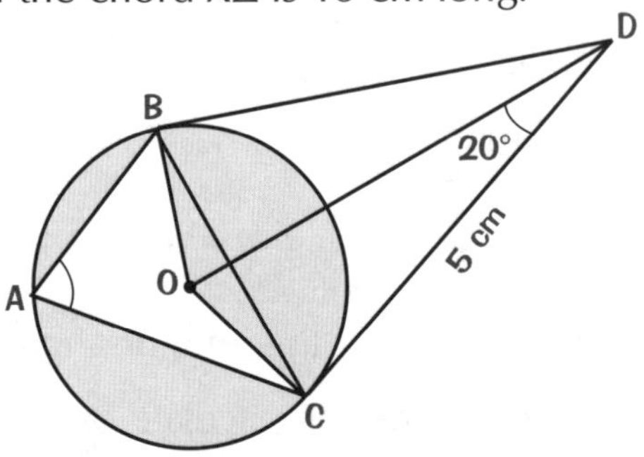

Questions on Bearings

A compass always points North...
It's easy to get lost here so always follow these 2 easy rules.

1) BEARINGS are always measured clockwise FROM the northline.

2) You should give all bearings as 3 FIGURES, even the small ones.

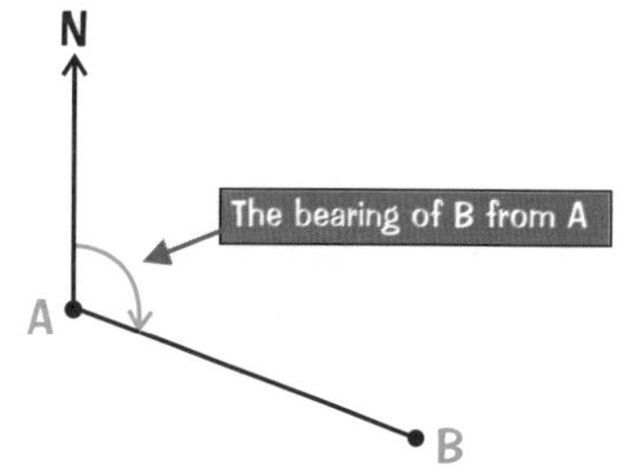

Q1 State or measure the bearing of:

a) Y from X
b) X from Y
c) Z from Y
d) Y from Z.

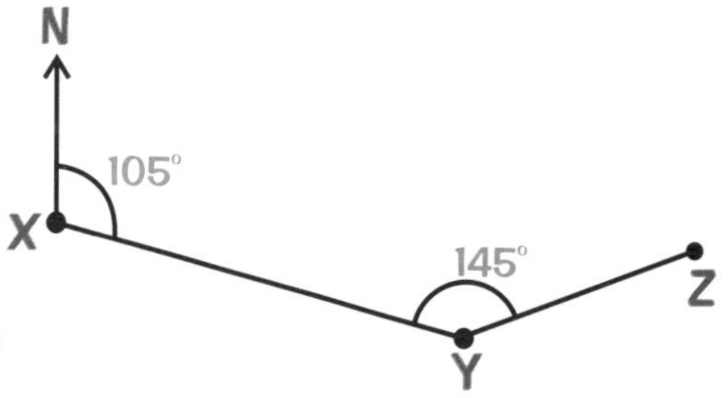

Q2 Using the same bearings as the last question, make an accurate scale drawing of X, Y and Z, when the distance XY is 10 km and YZ is 4 km. By measurement find:

a) the distance XZ
b) the bearing of Z from X
c) the bearing of X from Z.

You'll want to draw some extra North Lines or you won't get anywhere.

Q3 This is a map of the Channel Islands.

a) Which island is furthest west?
b) Which island is due east of Guernsey?
The dots show the airports.
c) What bearing is needed to fly from Jersey to Guernsey? How far is it?
The flight from Jersey to Alderney goes via Sark.
d) What is the bearing for the first leg of the journey?
e) What is the bearing for the second leg of the journey?
f) Calculate the total distance flown from Jersey to Alderney.

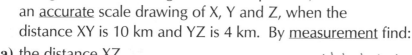

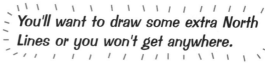

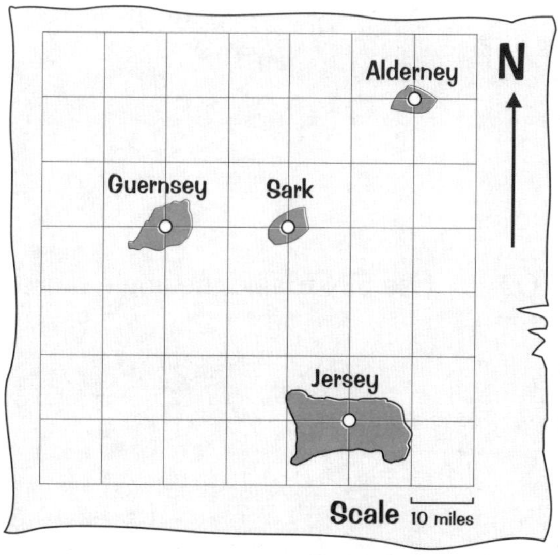

Q4 One afternoon I set out from home and walked 3 km on a bearing of 075°. Then I turned due south-east and walked 5 km. Make an accurate scale drawing of this walk.

a) How far did I get from home?
b) What bearing should I have used to get home in a straight line?

Q5 Points L, M and N have coordinates (1,3), (5,4) and (5,1) respectively. Draw x and y-axes, both going from 0 to 6, and plot these points. Use your protractor to measure the bearing of:

a) M from L
b) N from M
c) M from N
d) L from N.

Questions on Trigonometry

You really need to know your trigonometric formulas — you'll struggle without them.

An EASY WAY to remember the THREE formulas is to write "SOH CAH TOA" before you start — then turn the most suitable into a FORMULA TRIANGLE.

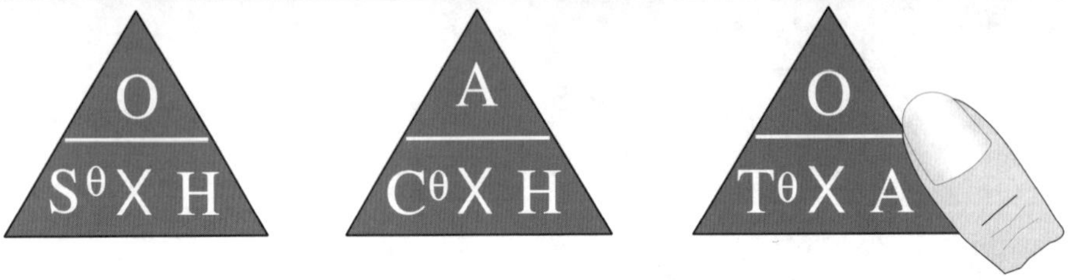

Q1 Use TAN to find the angle or side labelled with a letter.

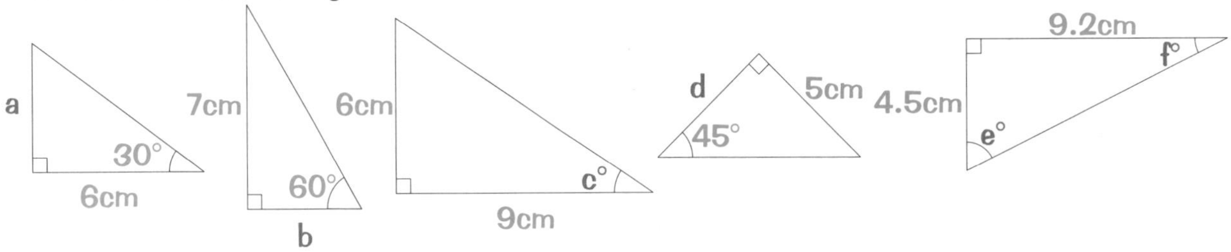

Q2 Use COS to find the angle or side labelled with a letter.

Don't try and do it all in your head — you're gonna have to get your pen out and label the sides. You'll find it loads easier to see what's going on.

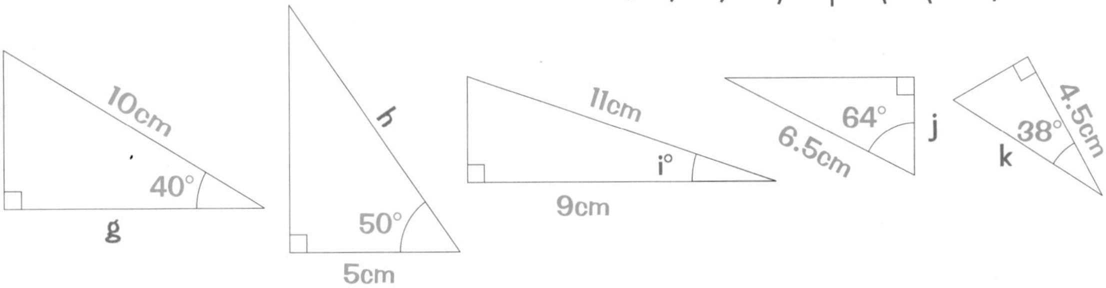

Q3 Use SIN to find the angle or side labelled with a letter.

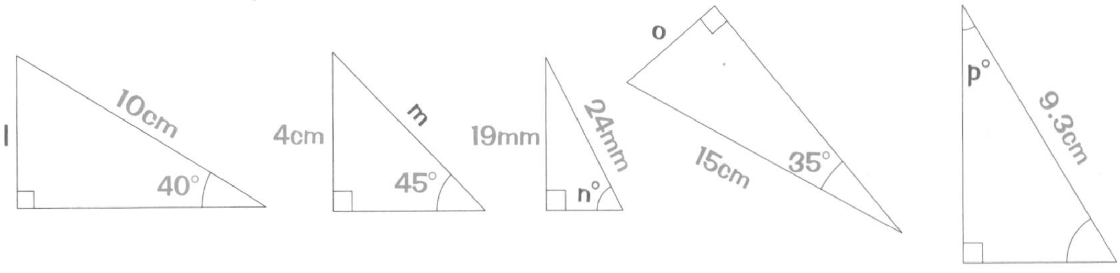

Q4 Choose the most suitable ratio to find the lettered angles and sides.

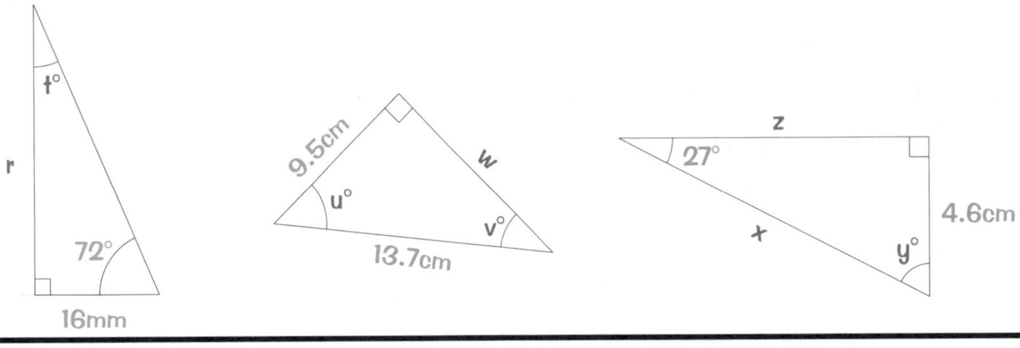

Questions on Trigonometry

Don't worry, these questions are just more of the same — except they've got prettier pictures. Don't forget to label the sides, though.

Q5 Mary was lying on the floor looking up at the star on top of her Christmas tree. She looked up through an angle of 55° when she was 1.5 m from the base of the tree. How high was the star?

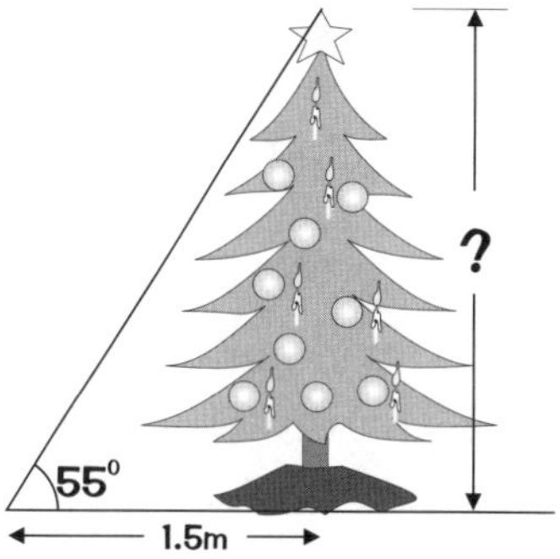

Q6 Mr Brown took his dog for a walk in the park. The dog's lead was 2 m long. The dog ran 0.7 m from the path Mr Brown was walking on, as shown in the diagram.

What angle did the lead make with the path?

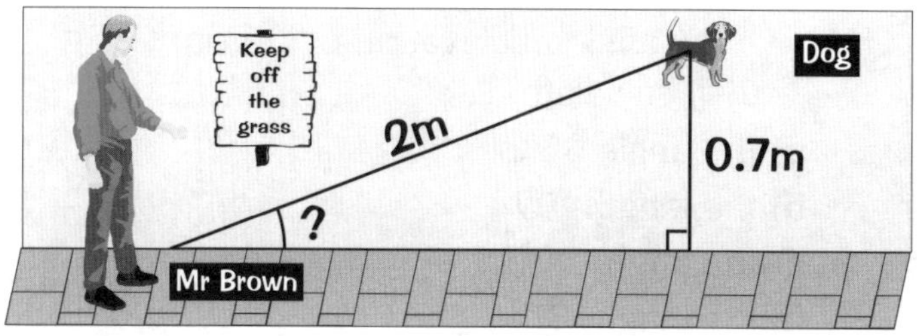

Q7 A coastguard on a cliff top saw a boat in trouble at sea. His viewpoint was 156 m high. The angle of depression that the coastguard looked along was 25°.

What distance was the boat from:

a) the base of the cliff?

b) the coastguard?

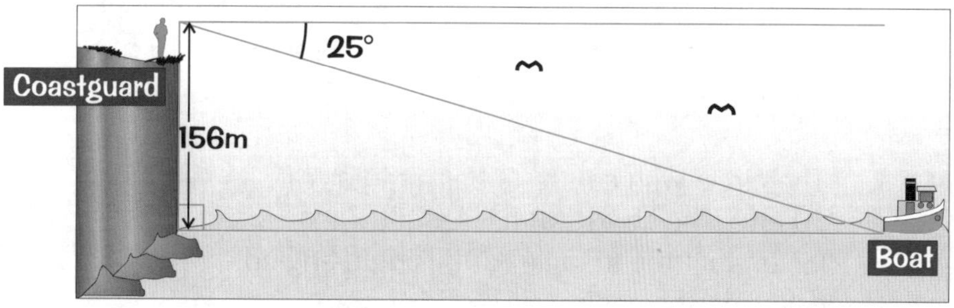

Remember, the angle of <u>depression</u> is always the <u>same</u> as the angle of <u>elevation</u>.

Q8 A boy walked diagonally across a rectangular field and measured the distance as 95 m. The line he walked on made an angle of 40° with the longer edge of the field.

a) Draw a <u>rough sketch</u> of the field and the boy's path across it.

b) Calculate the length and width of the field.

c) Calculate the area of the field.

Q9 A window cleaner with an extending ladder has to clean windows on two levels of a building. For the lower level his ladder must reach to 3.5 m. For the higher level it must reach 7 m. If the base of the ladder is always 2.5 m from the wall what angle is made with the horizontal when used for:

a) the lower level?

b) the upper level?

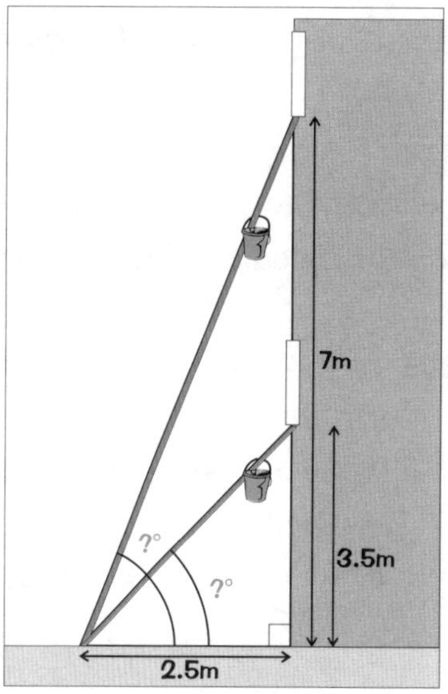

Questions on Trigonometry

These darn triangles seem to get <u>everywhere</u>, including the Exam — so make sure you can do <u>everything</u> on the last two pages, because you're gonna need it all.

Q10 Two fell tops are 1.5 km apart horizontally. One is 720 m high and the other is 340 m high. Find:

a) the difference in height between them

b) the angle of elevation looking from the lower to the higher fell.

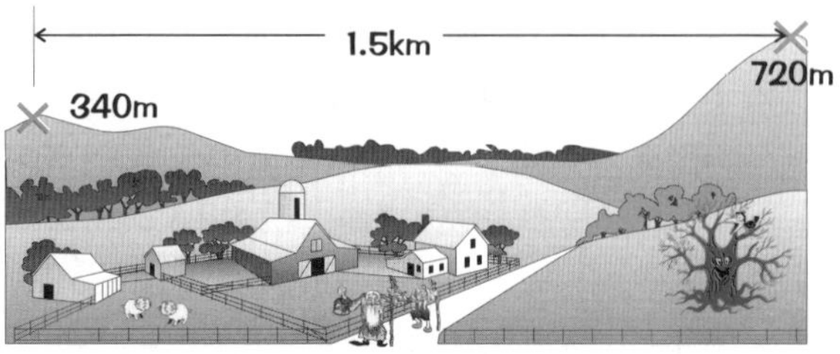

Q11 If the angle of elevation of D from C is 27°, calculate:

a) the angle BDC

b) the length AD

c) the angle DBC

d) the length BC.

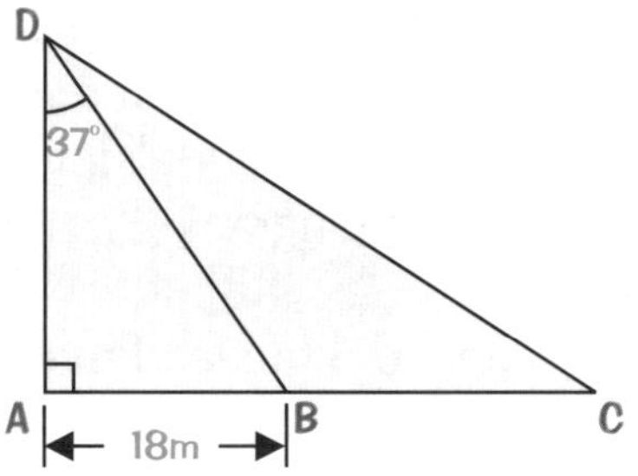

Q12 The points P(1,2), Q(4,2) and R(4,-3) when joined together form a right-angled triangle.

a) Draw a rough sketch of the triangle, labelling the length of each side.

b) <u>Without measuring</u>, calculate the angle RPQ.

c) <u>Deduce</u> angle PRQ.

Q13 The circle with centre O has a radius of 10 cm. The chord AB has length $\sqrt{200}$. Given that the triangle AOB is right-angled, calculate the angle ABO.

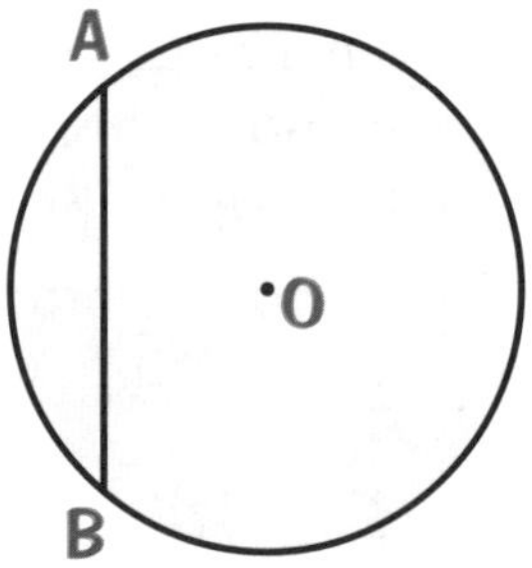

Don't let that <u>circle</u> put you off — it's a <u>normal question</u> really. Draw in the rest of the triangle. You've got all the sides, so all you need to do is <u>choose the formula</u>. How nice.

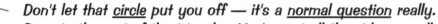

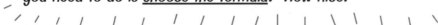

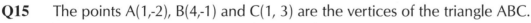

Q14 A right-angled triangle XYZ has sides measuring 30 m, 40 m and 50 m.

a) Draw a <u>rough sketch</u> of the triangle, clearly labelling the hypotenuse.

b) Calculate the size of the smallest angle.

Q15 The points A(1,-2), B(4,-1) and C(1, 3) are the vertices of the triangle ABC.

a) On graph paper, <u>plot</u> the points A, B and C.

b) By adding a suitable horizontal line, or otherwise, calculate the angle CAB.

c) Similarly calculate the angle ACB.

d) By using the fact that the interior angles of a triangle add up to 180° work out the angle ABC.

Questions on Trigonometry

If you want to get full marks, you'll need a good diagram. If they've been mean and haven't provided one then draw your own and don't forget to label the sides O, A, and H.

Q16 David wants to work out the height of his house. By counting rows of bricks he estimates that the bottom of the roof is 10 m above the ground. The width of the house is 8 m. Also, the angle made at the top of the roof is 90°.
What is the height of David's house?

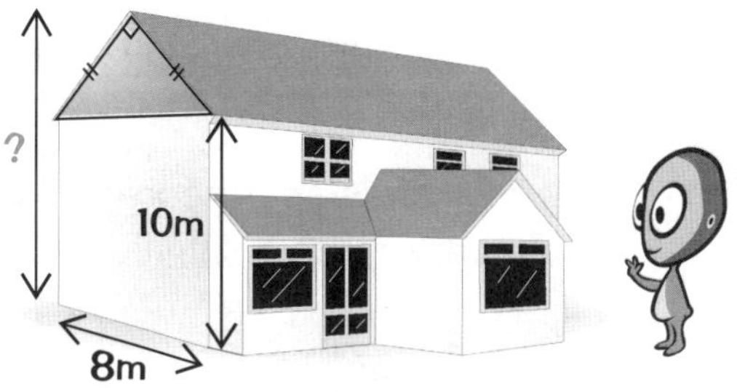

Q17 A girl walked diagonally across a rectangular field and measured the distance as 220 m. The line she walked on made an angle of 30° with the longer edge of the field.

a) Draw a rough sketch of the field and the girl's path across it.

b) Calculate the length and width of the field.

c) Calculate the area of the field.

Q18 The base of a cone has a radius of 7 cm. The angle ABO is 72°.

a) Work out the height of the cone OA.

b) A similar cone has a base radius of 14 cm. What is the height of this cone?

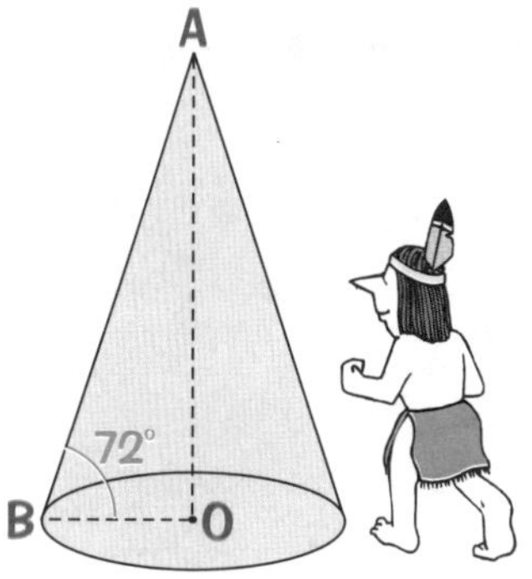

Remember to check that your answer is sensible.

Q19 John runs in a north-west direction from X for six miles to point Y. He then turns and runs in a south-west direction for eight miles to point Z.

a) Draw a rough sketch of John's route.

b) Write down the size of angle XYZ.

c) Calculate the length XZ.

Q20 A regular octagon is shown on the right. The centre O is 5 cm from the vertex P. Q is a point in the centre of one side.

a) By considering the angles at the centre of the octagon, find the size of the angle QOP.

b) Calculate the length of one side of the octagon.

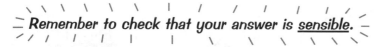

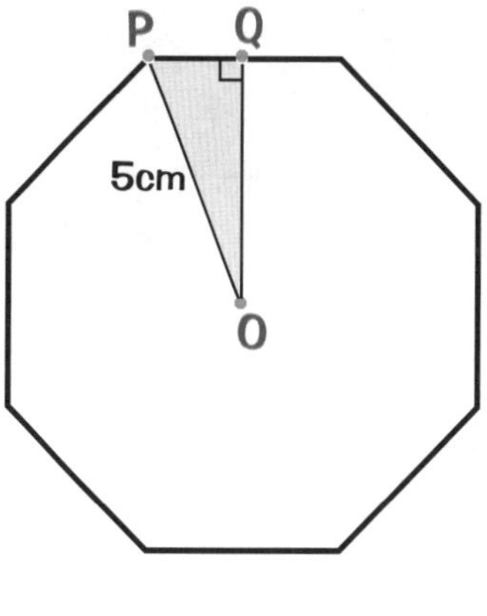

Q21 P is the point (10, 15), O is the origin.

a) Calculate the angle between OP and the positive y-axis.

b) Using your answer to part **a)** work out the distance from O to P.

Questions on Pythagoras' Theorem

If you're as big a fan of Pythagoras as me, you'll ignore him and use this method instead:

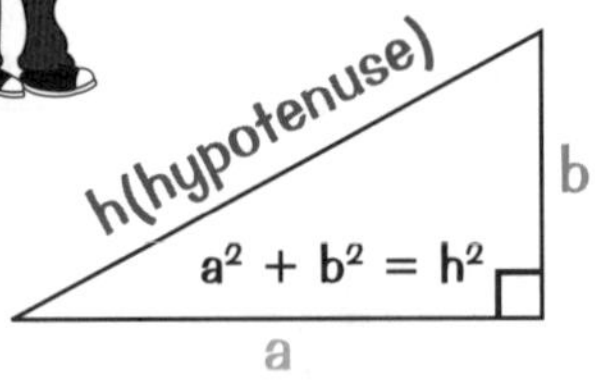

The Simple Three-Step Method

1) SQUARE the two numbers that you are given.
2) To find the longest side, ADD the two squared numbers.
   To find a shorter side, SUBTRACT the smaller one from the larger.
3) Take the SQUARE ROOT. Then check that your answer is sensible.

Q1 Using Pythagoras' theorem, calculate the length of the third side in these triangles, giving your answers to 3 significant figures.

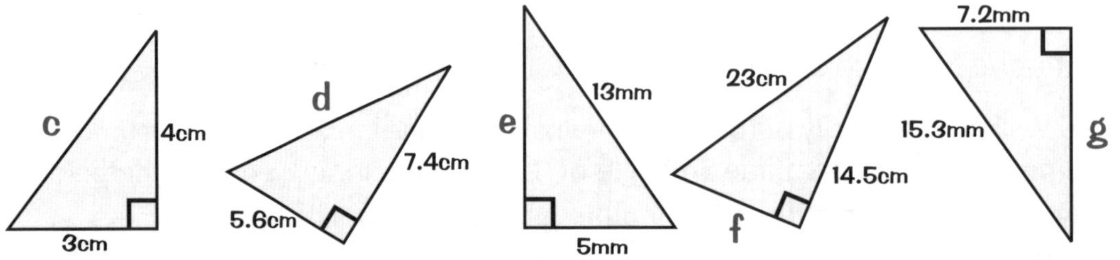

Q2 Using Pythagoras' theorem, work out which of these triangles have right angles.

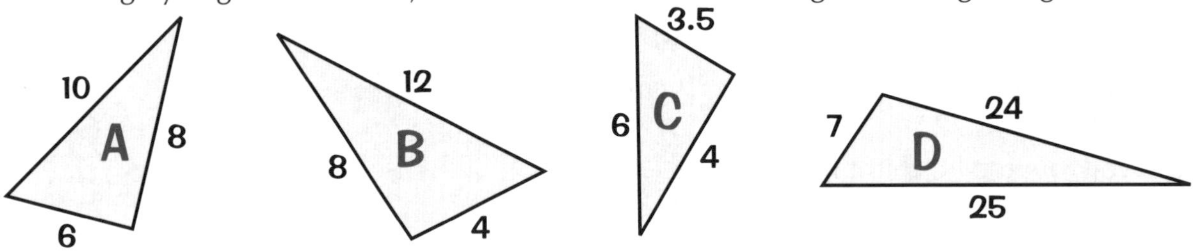

Q3 Calculate the missing lengths in these quadrilaterals.

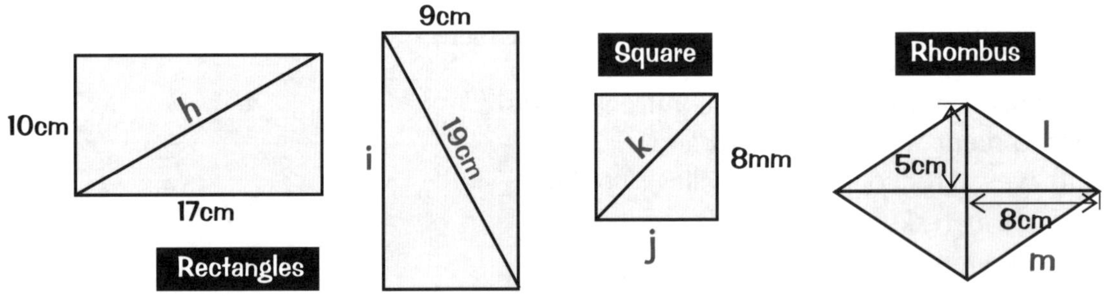

Q4

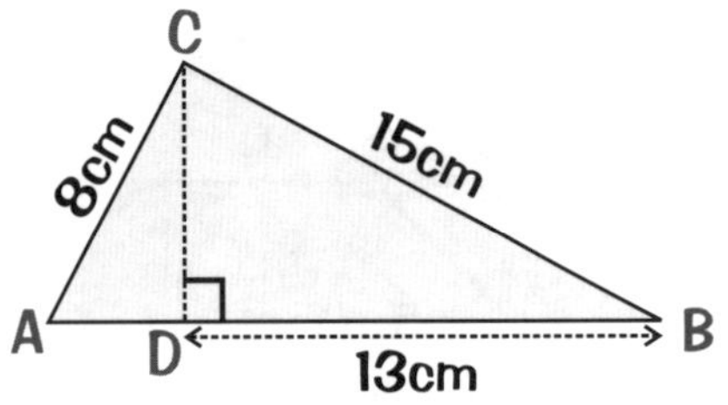

Find:
a) the height CD of this triangle
b) the length AD
c) the whole base length AB
d) the area of triangle ABC.
e) Is the triangle ABC right-angled ?

Q5 Find:
a) the length WX
b) the length WZ
c) the area of triangle WXZ.

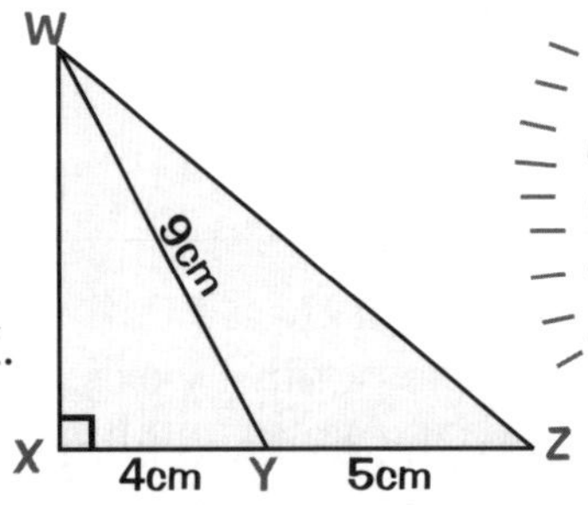

When there's more than one triangle, it's a bit harder to tell which side is which. Your best bet is to draw each triangle separately as you're using it — that way you'll get less muddled up.

Questions on Pythagoras' Theorem

You may have noticed that <u>none of these questions involve angles</u> — I guess that Mr Pythagoras wasn't too keen on them. So before you go reaching for that SIN button on your calculator, think again...

Q6 A builder has to reach the roof of a house 15 m high. His ladder is 20 m long. How far away from the house must the <u>foot of the ladder</u> be placed?

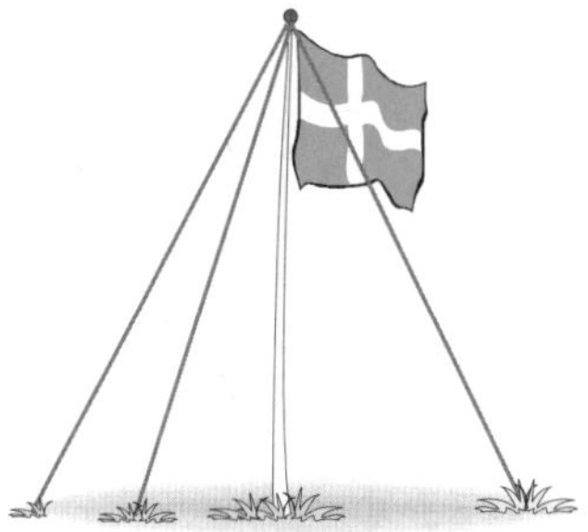

Q7 A flagpole is 6.5 m high and has 3 stay lines from the top to the ground. If the stay lines are 8, 9 and 10 m long how far from the foot of the flagpole must each one be secured?

Q8 A farmer has an oddly shaped field, as shown in the diagram, divided into two right-angled triangles. What length of fencing does he need to go all round the <u>perimeter</u> (not across the middle)?

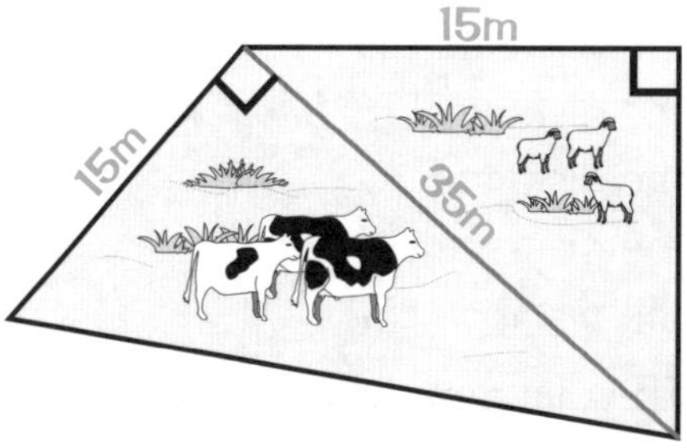

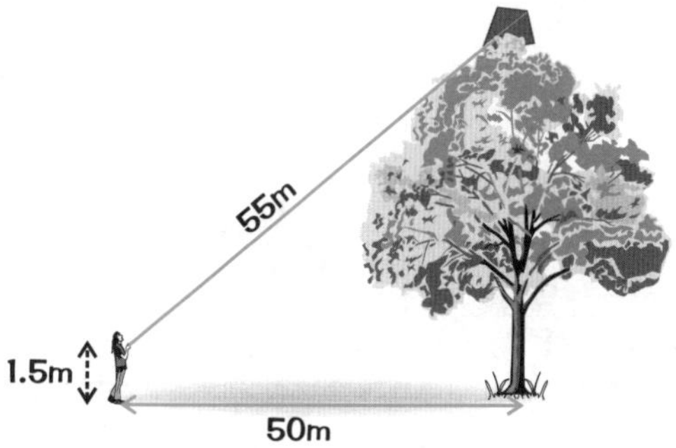

Q9 Jane was flying her kite on a string 55 m long, as shown. She is 1.5 m tall and was standing 50 m from the base of the tree. How tall must the tree be if Jane's kite could get <u>tangled in the top</u>?

Well, there's lots of practice to be had here, whether you want it or not. Still, once you've battled your way through all of these, you'll
a) be bored out of your mind
b) have another topic under your belt.

Q10 The doorway of a tent is an <u>isosceles</u> triangle, as shown. The height of the pole is 1.2 m and the distance from the base of the pole to the canvas is 56 cm. Find:

a) the length of the canvas from pole top to ground

b) the area of the doorway.

You'll be a lot better off if you draw diagrams for questions 11 & 12.

Q11 A ship leaves port and steams 10 km <u>due north</u>. It then turns and steams 12 km <u>due east</u>. How far is it from port now?

Q12 How long is the line that joins the points A (2,1) and B (8,2)?

Questions on Pythagoras' Theorem

Make sure that you only use Pythagoras' Theorem on right-angled triangles — it doesn't work too well on anything else. In fact it doesn't work at all.

Q13

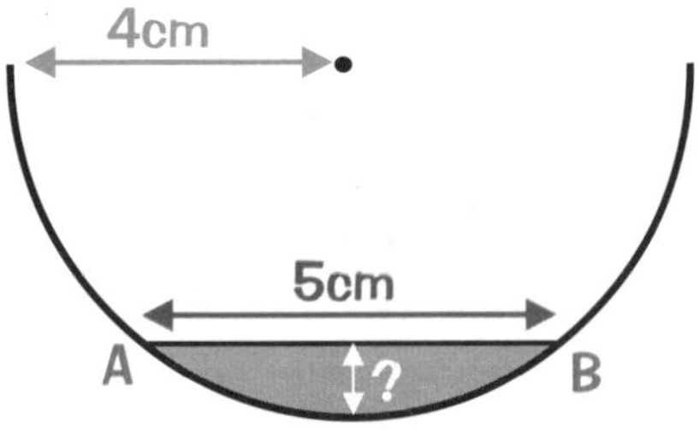

A cross-section of a piece of roof guttering is shown on the left. It is basically an open semicircle with a radius of 4 cm. The distance from point A to point B is 5 cm. Work out the greatest depth of the water.

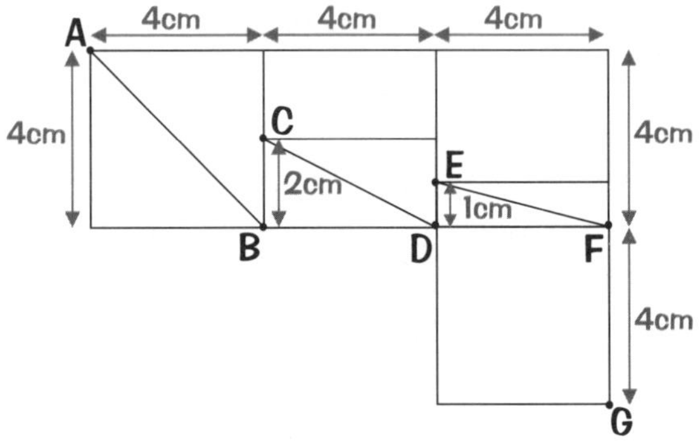

Q14 The diagram shows the relative positions of the points A, B, C, D, E, F and G. Find:

a) the distance AB
b) the distance CD
c) the distance EF
d) the distance AG
e) the distance CG
f) the distance EG.

Q15 The diagram shows a right-angled triangle with sides p, q and s. Complete the table:

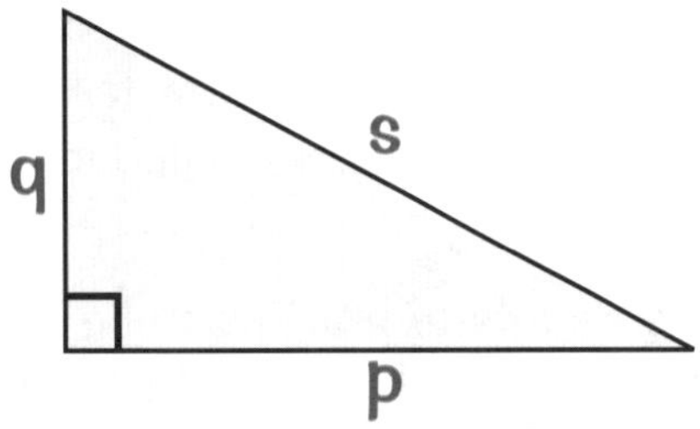

p	q	s
3		5
5		13
	6	10
	9	12.95
11	12	
1	1	

Q16 A fairground helter-skelter ride is basically a rolled up right-angled triangle. The ride pictured is 5 m high and, when thought of as a triangle, the base is 8 m long.

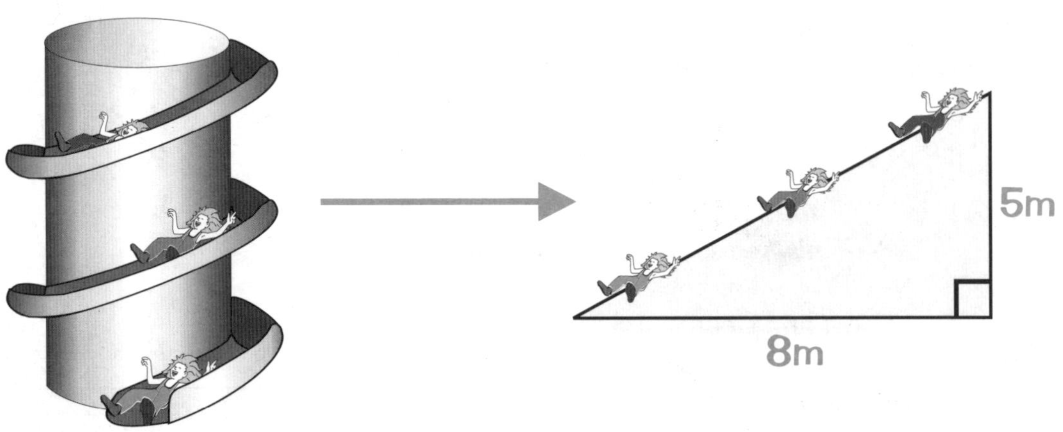

a) Work out, using Pythagoras' theorem, the length of the ride (the hypotenuse).
b) A girl took 6 seconds to descend from the top to the bottom. Calculate her average speed.